Alex Jenkins has worked in offices around London for the last ten years and has not yet overthrown top-level management. His weakness is taking on too much work. In five years he sees himself sat where you are now.

Stephen Morrison is a comedy scriptwriter for both television and radio. He has worked in a number of London offices where his main job was receptionist. His weaknesses are poor timekeeping and the hornpipe.

THE REGIONAL ACCOUNTS DIRECTOR

of

FIRETOP MOUNTAIN

ALEX JENKINS AND STEPHEN MORRISON

BANTAM PRESS

LONDON · TORONTO · SYDNEY · AUCKLAND · JOHANNESBURG

TRANSWORLD PUBLISHERS
61–63 Uxbridge Road, London W5 5SA
A Random House Group Company
www.rbooks.co.uk

First published in Great Britain
in 2008 by Bantam Press
an imprint of Transworld Publishers

A CIP catalogue record for this book
is available from the British Library.

ISBN 9780593062074

Addresses for Random House Group Ltd companies outside the UK
can be found at: www.randomhouse.co.uk
The Random House Group Ltd Reg. No. 954009

The Random House Group Limited supports The Forest Stewardship
Council (FSC), the leading international forest-certification organization. All our
titles that are printed on Greenpeace-approved FSC-certified paper carry the FSC logo.
Our paper procurement policy can be found at
www.rbooks.co.uk/environment

Typeset in 11.5/13 Palatino by
Falcon Oast Graphic Art Ltd.

Printed and bound in Great Britain by
Clays Ltd, Bungay, Suffolk

2 4 6 8 10 9 7 5 3 1

Dedicated to Matthew Morrison for good service 1934–96 and to Scarlett Jenkins – may you never have to enter data for an hourly wage.

ACKNOWLEDGEMENTS

Respectful salutes to Steve Jackson and Ian Livingstone, J. R. R. Tolkien, the Brothers Grimm and Homer's *Iliad*. Apologies to Rudyard Kipling.

Special thanks to: Blake Cuthbert, Sarah 'Enigmamatic' Emsley, Sesmin Ewing, Trudi Jenkins, the Jenkinses in the Shire, Rebecca Jones, Mave Morrison, the Morrisons of the icy north, Tom Poland, the Blue Posts, the Bricklayers Arms and the Mug House (our London offices), Mark Richards, Susan Rogers, Tomislav Tomić, Tom Whiteley, Kieran Williams, and James Taylor at Avalon.

INTRODUCTION

Welcome to *The Regional Accounts Director of Firetop Mountain*, a choose-your-own-adventure-style parody where YOU are the employee!

In this book, YOU take on the role of a data-entry temp and must uncover the dark secrets that lie hidden at the heart of the Firetop Mountain offices. Whether you succeed or fail in your quest depends entirely on the choices YOU make!

During the course of your adventure you will encounter many outlandish co-workers and colleagues. If you ever need background information on the member of staff you are dealing with, you can refer to the Office Bestiary at the back of this book. If you are unable to work proactively with a colleague, your only option may be to fight!

Your route through the Firetop Mountain offices will also test your adventurer's luck, and for this you will need to equip yourself with two dice and a pencil before you begin.

Now turn the page to learn how to fight . . .

HOW TO FIGHT

Ahoy there, office adventurer!

Throughout this book you will have encounters that require you to fight with certain creatures. By 'fight' we mean 'pretend dice fight' and not 'real fight' like when the pub closes.

If you are victorious in fighting any creature, you may pass on to the next part of the book. If you are defeated, you must return to the start. If you cheat, you are only cheating yourself.

Victories are decided by which fighter has the greatest Fight Score. Now let's work out YOUR unique Fight Score!

Office work involves filing, emailing and colleague surveillance: this requires Aptitude. Roll two dice and add up the score. This is your overall Aptitude rating. Make a note of this in the box marked APTITUDE in your CV (page xi).

While temping you have to spend hours doing data entry, pretending to do data entry and working out how much money you've earned since you arrived in the morning: this requires Endurance. Now roll two dice and add up the score. This is your overall Endurance rating. Make a note of this in the box marked ENDURANCE in your CV.

Your office career will frequently require you to call in sick and lie about dental appointments when you go to job interviews. Being believed requires Office Luck. Now roll two dice and add up the score. This is your overall Office Luck rating. Make a note of this in the box marked OFFICE LUCK in your CV.

Every time you fight, you will need to work out a new Fight Score. This is done by rolling two dice, then adding this total to your combined Aptitude and Endurance rating.

You will then need to calculate your opponent's Fight Score by adding together their Aptitude and Endurance ratings, and adding this figure to the total of two rolled dice.

Whoever has the greatest overall Fight Score will emerge the victor. If you lose the fight, you must return to the start of the book and begin your adventure again.

You may encounter a creature you could easily slay in a fight, even if you came across one in the real world. A fairy is one example of an 'easy win' opponent. If you feel your opponent falls into this category, you may as well proceed to the next part of the adventure. It's on the house.

Adventure Curriculum Vitae

Name:		
Aptitude:	**Endurance:**	**Office Luck:**

Items Retained in Cloak:

- -
- -

Curses Collected:

- -
- -
- -
- -
- -

Notes:

- -
- -
- -
- -
- -
- -
- -

In the underbelly of a city where cutpurse and peddler creep through the streets like vines is . . . a temping agency.

The agency is housed amongst a shanty town of Portakabins on the drab outskirts of the financial district. Vagrant temps squat in the filthy gutters, telling their word-per-minute speed to anyone who passes.

You are one such temp. Smart-casual in appearance, with an arsenal of three white tops, you can blend into the background of any office with a chameleonic prowess that has earned you the nickname 'the Temp'.

Yet times are hard, and for the last six weeks your regular agency has failed to find you employment, leaving you poverty-stricken and in dire need of money. Even the street peddlers no longer try to sell you their wares. Desperation has driven you to this foul part of town to beg for work.

Pushing open the rickety door of the temping agency, you ignore the squalor of the office and sit down on a cold iron stool.

Despite your impressive CV, the recruitment consultants shake their heads grimly at the prospect of finding you work. Half-crazed with hunger, you plead that you will take anything they have. Anything.

The consultants shoot nervous glances at each other as the office manager takes you quietly to one side.

'Well . . . there is one possibility,' he murmurs. 'It's a day's data-entry work. The hours are long and little is known of the company. There isn't a vacancy right now, but I can guarantee the client will be looking for some new blood before the day is out.'

This plum role could be yours for the taking if you succeed in answering one question: can you start tomorrow?

Nodding in agreement, you pass the interview with flying colours and the office manager hands you the address details. You read the company name aloud:

'Firetop Mountain plc.'

This spooks a ratty-looking consultant at the next desk, who lets out a shriek and drops his telephone into a bowl of gruel. Ignoring him, you leave the agency feeling elated. You head home to iron a top and turn in early for the day that awaits you.

The next morning you wake at dawn, pack a simple lunch of nuts and berries and trek for many hours, finally locating the Firetop Mountain office.

Sticking out incongruously from the surrounding buildings, the office is a boxy concrete eyesore. Your eyes gaze higher up the structure and you see that the architecture of the upper floors is inconsistent with the lower ones. They appear to have been cut from the living rock, as if someone had whittled a tastelessly ornate cathedral out of a mountain.

In accordance with temp lore, you check your watch to

make sure you're not early, then boldly approach the front door.

Turn to **2**.

2

The gnarled oak door of the Firetop Mountain office is weather-scarred and set into a roughly hewn stone wall. As you approach, the door looms over you. You gaze upwards at the building's lofty architecture. The building's lofty architecture looms over you. Protruding from the stone wall are two plastic buttons: one marked RECEPTION, the other marked 240V. The two plastic buttons loom over you.

To press the buzzer marked RECEPTION, turn to **184**.

To press the buzzer marked 240V, turn to **74**.

3

Down and down you go, constricted in a cramped container, precious lifeblood flowing from your back.

With desperate trembling hands you pull out your mobile phone. It has no signal but you manage to use it as a light.

Your weak beam darts from corner to corner of the container, settling at last on the body of a woman, a timesheet clutched in her dead hands. You are clearly not the first temp to have fallen into this trap.

You're about to scream when you hear a lift *ping* and you stop descending and start wheeling forward again. A familiar voice says, 'Roll on weekend' and you realize you've accidentally locked yourself in the tea lady's trolley!

You open a small hatch in the side of the trolley and peer through it to see that you are being pushed through a dank dungeon towards a security door. A noise like the steady beat of a slave-ship drum grows louder and louder.

On the door, etched into the steel, are two words:

SERVER ROOM.

Turn to **200**.

4

You bend down to examine the payslip and an arrow hits you squarely in the bottom through your dull grey cape.

You have unwittingly fallen into a poverty trap! Lose 3 OFFICE LUCK points but gain 1 Arrow in the Bottom.

Turning the air blue, you continue towards the doors.

Turn to **52**.

5

The treefolk's sales office is a slow-motion bustle of activity. One tree is dialling a number on a telephone, but doing it so ponderously that the line cuts off before he completes it. Behind him, a calendar shows a sapling with the caption MISS FEBRUARY.

Another tree has just sealed a big deal and plods at glacial speed towards a reward bell fastened to the opposite wall. They all look so healthy that getting a bough from any of them is going to be like taking candy from a Bengal tiger.

While you scan the office for a tree likely to be an easy pushover, one tree with a stork in its branches approaches.

'Hooooom! I . . . am . . . doing . . . a . . . sponsored . . . stork. It . . . is . . . to . . . see how . . . many . . . days . . . I . . . can . . . keep . . . a . . . stork . . . in . . . my . . . branches . . . Will . . . you . . . sign . . . my . . . form?'

To sponsor the deciduous donor, turn to **187**.

To ignore the philanthropic forest dweller, turn to **213**.

6

Striding through a candy-cane installation, you arrive eventually at a door made of biscuit with the letters IHR iced on it in pink writing.

After a gentle tap you hear a woman's voice croak, 'Enter!'

A waft of cinnamon greets your nostrils as you enter the Inhuman Resources Department and spy a kindly

old crone carefully adjusting a health bar on a gingerbread desk.

She smiles up at you from under the brim of a pointy hat. She's clearly some sort of witch, but you sense she is a nice one.

'Are you here about the ants?' she chirps. You shake your head. 'That's the trouble with biscuit furniture, you see – always with the ants!'

You think this strange as there are no ants in the room. Furthermore you are perturbed by a windchime made out of various Brackwurst.

'What's your cake name?' the old hag asks distractingly. You look blank. 'Your cake name? Come on. Work it out. It's easy to do. You simply take the first part of your mother's favourite cake then add it to the last part of your favourite cake. Mine's "Black Forest Battenberg", see? It's a bit of fun.'

To work out your cake name, turn to **246**.

Or shun such office tomfoolery by going to **140**.

7

Biding your time, you move towards two empty desks, shielding your face from a cluster of pixies who are playing office dodgeball with a dead bee.

You are about to sit when your hand is slapped by an unseen force. You watch as the keyboard types a spread-sheet on its own – like an Excel pianola.

The desk opposite the invisible worker is the worst in the office as it offers a view of its screen to a management office behind you. You sit at it, feeling so lonely you can't even play solitaire.

On the screen is a familiar spreadsheet, and a collection of parchment scrolls sit next to the keyboard, waiting to have their data entered.

Suddenly the phone at your desk begins to ring! This is a worst-case scenario for anyone in a new office. After twenty-seven rings you realize you must act fast.

To answer the phone in this alien office, go to **70**.

To busy yourself entering fantastical data instead, go to **123**.

8

'The neck, the neck, look at the neck,' barks an auditor putting on prescription sunglasses. 'It's him him him.'

In a heartbeat, all the feral auditors are belligerently yapping, 'Him! Him! Him!' in your face.

It seems in the half-light they have mistaken you for Jessie from the ground floor, the source of much of the impenetrable filing that has devolved them to their current wild state.

Their dextrous paws grab your body as they howl about teaching YOU a thing or two about accountable filing systems.

Turn to **21**.

9

You continue to walk down the long dark tunnel.

Cramp kicks into your legs, so you turn and walk backwards for a while to break the journey up. After a while you realize this method only really works with swimming.

On you press: **149**.

10

The feral auditors are a playful bunch, but you don't have the time to play with them and don't want to spend the next seven years clearing up their nonsense with a little trowel.

You distract the pack by throwing half a tennis ball in their midst, then bound away.

Turn to **19**.

11

You knock and enter, which is the same as bursting in unannounced.

Turn to **110**.

12

With the accident book of the *Golden Scart* safe in your hands, you make for the round blue door.

The decktop fax machine whirs into life and the high elf with the eyepatch waits eagerly as paper slowly judders out.

As you step through the door you see his face drop as

he holds up a fax with a single black spot on it. 'No way can this be good,' he says.

Turn to **115**.

13

Every creature has its weapon trained on you as they stand in a silence broken only by the bleating of a meek lamb. A drow elf advances, halberd raised.

'We will not tolerate wolf cryers,' he hisses. 'Especially those who mistreat a lovely lamb.'

The halberd finds your hood and the drow elf stands poised to rip it off. 'STOP!' cries a nearby voice. 'I too have been harassed by this creature.'

Everyone searches the room for the speaker.

'Over here,' says a voice from the desk opposite, and a block of Post-It notes waves itself in the air. 'For many moons I have been mooned at. And I have felt alone.'

With much force the invisible worker throws a calculator at the shapeshifter, causing it to turn into two wargs doing it.

ZIP, ZIP, ZIP! A volley of arrows fills the air and the shapeshifter is felled.

'Huzzah! Huzzah! Huzzah!'

As a dryad clears the shapeshifter's desk, you feel a grateful invisible hand on your shoulder and a voice whispers in your ear, 'It is no longer safe for you here, colleague. Leave for the toilets now, avoiding the kitchen at all costs.'

Turn to **137**.

14

You enter the gents' toilet. With a moan of despair you realize there are no paper towels with which to bandage your back! You tug frantically at the rotary hand towel, but it just goes round and round.

In desperation you kick open the cubicle and lurch for the toilet roll.

This is treated as an aggressive act by the leathery-faced man on the toilet, who kicks out at you with a polished brogue!

LEATHERY-FACED MAN   APTITUDE 2   ENDURANCE 4

If you defeat the fierce-footed foe, turn to **262**.

15

You head down the corridor and feel a steep drop in temperature. Your breath mists up in front of you as you continue past a motivational poster of emperor penguins pitching into an icy sea. COURAGE, reads the caption.

Fired up by the bravery of the penguins, you press on until you yourself come to an icy lake which blocks your way, which is unusual for a listed building.

To turn back, turn to **6**.

To brave the icy depths, turn to **266**.

16

A small group of drow elves are busy gossiping around the water cooler. As you approach, the elves stop speaking and lean on their bows while gazing at the floor.

You are forced to endure this awkward pause (**263**), unless you speak Elvish, that is (**258**).

17

You listen to the voice, which sounds like it's coming down the wrong end of a drainpipe. Whoever's speaking must have an abhorrently long neck.

The echoing voice confesses to improper filing, improper archiving, improper binding and sexual conduct with a colleague.

His latter confession involves far too much detail about someone only referred to as 'Little Chicken'.

Feeling sordid, you get down to some work.

Turn to **18**.

18

You start entering employee tax data and realize you recognize some of the names of the workers. Workers you haven't seen for a long time.

Suddenly a wave of horror washes over you.

Your printer at home is low on paper!

Stealthily you skim a ream of foolscap from the nearest copier, making sure nobody notices. But what would it matter if they did? It happens all the time.

You stow the foolscap in your bag and sneak back to your desk, feeling a sense of triumph.

As a temp, you don't expect luxury furnishings, but your chair is definitely causing severe discomfort to your back. A flower of unease grows in your mind.

Something isn't right.

To follow up the bloom of apprehension and examine the terrible pain in your back, turn to **71**.

To make plans for the evening, turn to **54**.

19

Marching determinedly through the shadows of the labyrinth, you arrive at an alcove in which dusty tomes fill the many shelves. A strange monotone humming sound fills the room.

Upright on a dusty settee are two skeletons. One of the skeletons is pointing open-jawed at itself in what looks like a mocking gesture.

To hunt out the source of the humming, turn to **215**.

To study the skeletons, turn to **208**.

Furiously you butt at the glass, causing a thin web of cracks to form. Blood runs down your shirt from your shoulder as the accountant watches with selfish amusement.

Suddenly an axe splits the door (which is the same as knocking then barging in), and with terrified eyes you spy the assembled hordes of Firetop Mountain massed at the door, raging to get in.

Scanning the room desperately, your eyes fall on the Portal. Then you make the most important decision of your life.

Turn to **141**.

The feral auditors 'file' you by locking you in a cage with only an abacus to keep you sane. Eventually you die alone and in darkness. Your body will never be retrieved.

In a comical coincidence, the police will eventually 'file' your case under MISSING: PRESUMED DEAD. Your adventure ends here.

The office consists of many booths. Behind a row of screens you hear the tip-tap of computer keys from the hands of unseen workers. A tea lady is hobbling around with a big urn on wheels, filling the room with sugary steam.

Bernie Ditter settles you at a vacant booth then kneels

beside you and desperately grips your arm with bony knuckles.

'You must *not* leave this desk. The auditors . . . are in!' he hisses, searching your face with one white and one angry red eye.

You ask where you go for the toilet.

'We tend not to,' says Bernie Ditter. Casting your gaze around the room, you notice the concrete floor is sloped at a slight angle towards a gutter and immediately think the worst.

When you turn back, Bernie Ditter has disappeared.

Your chair is so uncomfortable, its previous owner was either a contortionist or a self-harmer, but the computer is on and the desk is supporting a stack of papers next to a well-thumbed introductory manual for temporary staff. It's a classic data-entry set-up and you feel right at home. It may be time to enter your first bit of data, but humans are bung full of free will and you are completely un-supervised.

To peer into the adjacent booth, turn to **207**.

To Google your own name, turn to **237**.

23

With their pitiless boss dead, the sales team keep their promise and reward you with an actual treefolk bough, which they pick up from a pile of hundreds littering the office floor.

'Hooom! We . . . cannot . . . thank . . . you . . . enough. The . . . gratitude . . . of . . . the . . . erm . . . trees . . . will . . . go . . . with . . . you . . . and . . . should . . . you . . . ever . . .'

There's really no need to listen to the woody windbags any more, so you make finger guns at them, pick up a few spare treefolk boughs just in case, and then leave.

Turn to **91**.

24

You locate the lift in the corridor. It accepts the stolen key-card and it isn't long before it arrives (thankfully empty). Pushing the button for the first floor, you wonder what manner of terrible creatures await you. The lift *ping*s on arrival at the first floor and you realize there is no turning back.

Do you take three deep breaths and brave yourself for what other-worldly horrors may await you on this floor (**254**)?

Or do you rub your proboscis with your forelegs, checking instantly in all directions for danger (**249**)?

25

Remember the fiery pipefitter? Happy days.

You become convinced you're miles away from the proper adventure by now . . . until finally you arrive at the end of a tunnel: **206**.

You collapse on a pile of the wounded and the dead, as the creature that materialized from your blood evaporates in front of you, giving you two thumbs up as it leaves.

The Regional Accounts Director pounds against his protective glass in horror as you heave open the One File. Gasping for air, you begin to recite P45 incantations in alphabetical order.

'Aaarakson, Aailan, male. PAYE ref. 1073883,' you pant, and a typing gnome is resurrected from the mound of the dead, glows white and is swept happily through the Portal.

'*NO!*' screams the Regional Accounts Director, and begins hoofing the crack.

'Aak-sin-jen, Batang, female. PAYE ref. 1083043.'

A dead lizard PA rises as if from a power nap and floats peacefully into the Portal's cleansing light.

'Ailsbane, Gretel, female. PAYE ref. 1068550.' The spirit of the Wurst Witch drifts to the Portal, making a magic gesture and lifting your curse as it goes.

While you continue to set the office workers free, the Regional Accounts Director rifles through his desk like a burglar, desperate for a weapon.

One by one they pass, spirit or living, ever thankful for your selfless task. Even Jessie parades past in cheerful confusion like someone who has joined a conga but isn't sure why.

Orom the caretaker orc floats towards the Portal and places his biro next to you as he passes, starting something of a trend.

Soon you are standing next to a mountain of pens, when the Regional Accounts Director emerges from his desk with a box of cooks' matches.

'Chepstow, Helmfurt, male. PAYE ref. 1059433.' You speed up as a post-room centaur does gun fingers at you before trotting into the Portal.

'I will burn you! AAAAAAAAAAAAAAARGH!' screams the director, and you turn to see that he's accidentally set himself on fire.

The flames consume him. You continue hoarse-voiced to set your colleagues free.

The glass shatters as the accountant collapses against the curtains, which go up like a phoenix on nights. Coughing against the fumes, you continue through the Hs, desperate to get to the Zs.

By the time you free the last elf (with a lot of Zs in his name) the room is a raging box of flame and smoke. You stagger spluttering to the exit, and a slightly charred piece of paper wafts up in front of you. Straining your eyes through the smoke you stare at it.

It's your timesheet!

Turn to **128**.

Clasping the One File to your chest, you weave back down to ground level, where it dawns on you that the only way back is through the labyrinth. From memory you retrace your steps.

Over the place and round the point, down the bend and up the stoop, mid the scene and past the thing, up the gap and round the path . . .

. . . Until you arrive back at the photocopier, where an elf is talking sternly to a short, bespectacled troll.

To eavesdrop on the dispute, turn to **182**.

To steer clear, turn to **59**.

28

You stand firm in a classic 'no story today' pose, and the accountant sniffs his acceptance.

'Temps never care about who they work for,' he spits through gritted teeth. 'And to be honest, it did need some work.'

You stand motionless, racking your brain for a pithy quip to put this villain in his place. You can't think of anything and end up just standing in silence like a berk.

Visibly irritated with you, the accountant hits a flashing red button on his desk – and pages the entire building!

Turn to **155**.

29

As you press deeper you notice small stalagmites and stalactites have formed at the floor and roof of the tunnel. Wreathed in the shadows, they are silent and forbidding, giving the tunnel the appearance of a long-abandoned jaw.

Suddenly you make out the splish-splosh of many tiny feet.

You move towards the sound with great trepidation.

Turn to **196**.

30

Your rarest-of-the-rare AB blood sizzles in the Portal, causing the mob to freeze in a tableau of shock.

You search the room in anguish, but it seems no creature has emerged.

'There!' points a dwarf on a scooter, and every eye falls to the Portal's base.

Advancing on your behalf is a creature with the head of an ant . . . and the body of an ant!

Because you summoned it, this creature will fight for you until it is slain. In the unlikely event that this happens, you must then face the mob yourself!

ANT	APTITUDE 1	ENDURANCE 1
	VS	
ENTIRE STAFF OF LOWER ADMIN	APTITUDE 3	ENDURANCE 413

If you or your tag-team insect make it through, turn to **26**.

31

You are frozen with fear at the sight of the troll, who begins giving the tea lady an unwanted IT lesson. The lesson bores you to tears. You manage to stay awake only by reminding yourself you are in the presence of a troll.

'Now we've removed the blood clot, we'll get a power spike with the increased power surge. Not good. Spikes can subject your equipment to a potentially fatal excess of power.'

TROLL.

'If the surge doesn't blow something outright, it can progressively damage the PSU – power supply unit – and *other* components as well!'

TROLL.

'The plain filter powerboards you can buy at hardware stores are worse than useless. They give you the impression you're protected, when you basically aren't.'

TROLL TROLL TROLL TROLL TROLL.

The astonishingly dull troll drags what looks like a mighty Aztec gateway on castors into view.

'However, since we're dealing with a contained grid, moving the Portal *away* from the power source should stop the blackouts.'

The troll throws the contents of the cauldron at the gateway. There is a crashing strobe effect then a *DOOOOOOOOOOOOOOOOOOOOOOOOOOOooooooooooooo* sound as the room goes back to black.

'Come out the way,' says the troll impatiently to the tea lady as you flee the room in the blackness.

Turn to **233**.

32

Now accustomed to the previously fatal heat, you pull out your packed lunch of nuts and berries, to find it's been cooked into a roast-nut cutlet with hot-berry sauce. It's a mammoth culinary improvement on a previously humdrum meal. Gain 1 OFFICE LUCK point!

If you have a buzzard secreted within the folds of your cloak, turn to 53.

If you are unfettered with the bulk of a carrion bird, turn to 252.

33

You drop the hessian sack. The gorgon's head says a muffled 'Oi!' and starts lamenting again. Pleased that you decided not to cart a moaning head about all day long, you give the buzzard a playful wink and it nestles back into your cloak.

The familiar feathery bulk of the buzzard fills you with confidence, and you step boldly through the door into the eerie Labyrinth Department!

Turn to 210.

34

With an iron will, you breathe deeply until the bus of nausea pulls away from your stop. You resolve to appreciate your good health more often.

The fire sprite rolls its eyes sarcastically and leads you to Meeting Cabin A, which also has a strong nautical theme, like a seaside pub.

At the head of a long table, a stout black dwarf with a captain's hat sits amid a motley crew. You greet the dwarf, explaining that you are here to help with the hostile takeover.

'He can't hear you,' whinnies a unicorn with a hook for a horn. 'The takeover took his ears.'

'The takeover claimed my ears,' explains the captain dwarf loudly to everyone. 'It must be stopped today.'

The crew become rowdy and a troll missing an arm yells, 'It has my arm!'

'And my foot,' shouts a footless drow.

'And my ass!' shouts an orc with a wooden behind.

Suddenly the roof of the ship is torn away! Everyone points up and shouts, ''TIS A HOSTILE TAKEOVER!' and you realize that when they say 'hostile takeover' what they really mean is 'hostile Kraken'.

Turn to **259**.

35

With your hydration at an all-time low, you drink copiously from the water cooler. The water is fine! Feeling massive relief that it is not trick water, you glug cup after plastic cup of ice-cold water until the spout runs dry.

Gain 3 ENDURANCE points and an urgent need to visit a toilet.

Turn to **191**.

36

The Minotaur intern breathes excitably through its nostrils as you bluster something about just feeling a bit peaky.

It eyes you up and down with eyes like gas hobs on full.

'You fear me, wanderer. Do not deny it,' it says, with a farmyard quality to its voice. 'Such a pitiful race you are . . . offering virgins to avoid the wrath of our kind . . . always with the virgins, when you know what we really like? Well I'll tell you. Grass. Plain and simple. I mean it's not that hard, is it?'

Angry tears coast down the Minotaur's face as it says 'grass' again for emphasis.

Thinking on your feet, you reach into your pocket and offer the Minotaur your best crimson hanky as comfort, but it's like a red rag to a bull!

MINOTAUR INTERN   APTITUDE 8   ENDURANCE 12

If you defeat this beast of office burden, turn to **90**.

37

In the circumstances, you deduce that wishing for two thousand rubber moulds could be the best course of action. You address your mould-production-related wish directly to the djinn.

Turn to **273**.

38

For the next moments you struggle to garner information from the ranger.

Your conversation goes a bit like this.

You:	*Where are the treefolk, please?*
Ranger:	*It would be wise to keep on moving.*
You:	*Can you please direct me to the treefolk?*
Ranger:	*Moving on would be the wise option.*
You:	*In what direction are the treefolk?*
Ranger:	*The wise would keep . . .*
You:	*DON'T! Please stop saying that! Don't ever say that again!*
Ranger:	
You:	*Now where are the main treefolk, please?*
Ranger:	
You:	*Where is the office of the treefolk?*
Ranger:	
You:	*Treefolk, please?*
Ranger:	
You:	*Treefolk?*
Ranger:	
You:	*Fine! I'll go it alone.*
Ranger:	*Good.*

You venture into the forest without the assistance of an uppity ranger.

Turn to **251**.

39

Thinking quickly, you write *Good riddance to bad rubbish* in the card, then follow it up with *Just kidding* and close it off with eight exclamation marks.

Your punctuation is considered a laugh riot by the skeleton army, and they march out of the office with

a noise like a rack of snooker cues clattering on lino.
Turn to **120**.

40

Thanking all that is holy that you haven't alarmed the
canine accountants with an abnormal neck, you search
in your backpack for something to win them over.

If you have salvaged a pink holepunch from an
underwater realm, turn to **226**.

If you wish to offer your packed lunch of nuts and
berries, turn to **83**.

41

Staggering above deck, you come up against a row of
wailing crew members nursing freshly ripped limbs,
and suspect that something big has kicked off while
you convalesced. The sails are tattered and the mast
lies splintered across the deck. It appears that the
takeover was more hostile than anyone was prepared
for.

With a stroke of excellent fortune, the fire sprite has
been extinguished by a big wave and lies steaming on
the floor. Nobody notices as you prise the accident book
out of his doused hands and tiptoe surreptitiously to the
poop deck.

Turn to **12**.

42

You continue to traverse the tunnel.

Aside from an over-a-decade-old corpse wearing a

badge with the words PAM and WILSON on it, there is little of interest.

Tunnel on to **78**.

43

Irritably you correctly inform the sphinx that she is an arrow. She could not look more disgusted if you had broken into her desert paddock and weed on her cubs.

A heavy shower of water and mascara hits you and, looking up, you see the sphinx is crying. Clearly her inability to provide mind-bending riddles is a knock to her self-esteem.

'Cleverest of adventurers, take pity on the sphinx and grant me an exit interview before you pass. It's just so I can get a few pointers on where I'm going wrong.'

To ignore the sphinx's request, turn to **158**.

To grant her an exit interview, turn to **222**.

44

The waiting room is decadently furnished with opulent wooden sofas, and on one of the walls there hangs a framed motivational poster of bees working in a hive.

To investigate the poster, turn to **188**.

To sit down on an inviting sofa, turn to **95**.

45

You begin talking brightly with the albino receptionist, who soaks up the attention like arid soil. Gain 1 OFFICE LUCK point!

You soon run dry of small-talk, however, and lapse into a long awkward silence in which you both smile benignly for a few minutes, nodding gently at each other in the half-darkness. Eventually the receptionist points a luminous finger towards a door and asks you to wait in the waiting room.

Turn to **44**.

46

You stand sweating over the many slain carcasses of the feral auditors. Now you think about it, they're just another group of people helplessly caught up in the nefarious scheme of the Regional Accounts Director and didn't really deserve to die. Not all of them.

Adding them to your ever-growing list of creatures to avenge, you press deeper into the labyrinth in search of the One File.

Turn to **19**.

47

Glad to be past the sphinx, you push open the stone door to the One File room and breathe a sigh of wonder. Whoever designed the One File room was probably on glue.

The room is cathedral-tall, with a thick stone ledge weaving dizzily up to the ceiling with some very angry bends.

Tasteful halogen wall lights punctuate the darkness

as background muzak hums from unseen speakers, surfing the rocky acoustics.

In the centre of the room a dwarf dances eerily, basking in the shadows of a well-lit lift.

You could indeed use this lift (**150**).

Or climb the ledge instead (**181**).

48

So long is your journey in the lift that by the time you make it to the top you have bonded with both wizards in a big way.

Aside from their sexist vernacular, they are two regular, meat-and-potato wizards: honest guys here to install USB cauldrons on all of the company's PCs.

During a group hug, the less pale wizard, Grindmirth, realizes they've come in on the wrong day, which everyone finds hilarious.

No longer needing it, Grindmirth gives you his visitor's badge and high-fives you. Then Gorrin, the much paler of the two, gives you 'big tens' and the badge shimmers.

As they head back down in the lift you notice the badge now reads DIRECTOR.

Gain 2 OFFICE LUCK points.

Feeling brilliant and relaxed, you turn out on to a landing, then see a sight that almost stops your heart!

Turn to **62**.

49

The stout orc charges, weapon aloft.

'Hold your sword, Orom!' screams the tall one suddenly. The short one stops grumpily dead in his tracks. The kindly orc turns back to you. 'Weary temp, my name is Slinnk. Orom you have already met,' he sighs.

'We are caretaker orcs,' adds Orom.

'And the reason my colleague has not split your skull is that we have great use for you.'

Orom narrows his eyes slyly at you. God, it really stinks in here.

'You have done well to make it this far,' Slinnk continues. 'Sit and I will tell of the foul office politics that besmirch this wretched place in full atmospheric detail.'

'Or stand and I will tell you the abridged version,' butts in Orom.

Will you allow Slinnk to herald his long back-story (116)?

Or go for Orom's bullet-point version instead (247)?

50

In a dangerous office, the lowlier your role, the more invisible you are likely to be. Bearing this in mind, you pull on the rough cloak of lower admin.

With the hood up you could easily pass for elf, dwarf or lizard, depending on your bust size and height.

You leave the Wurst Witch's office through a door marked ADMIN STAFF and move down a hospital-like corridor towards a set of red double doors.

Yet halfway along you notice something curious on the floor. It's a payslip . . . which already has your name on!

Will you pick up the mysterious payslip (4)?

Or leave it where it lies (52)?

51

You clearly state that you are wishing for the tears of a djinn, except at the last moment you get sidetracked and, on a whim, wish for a better signal on your mobile phone. Four bars magically materialize on your mobile! Your signal strength is robust beyond belief!

You turn to show the supernaturally strong signal to the djinn, but he merely points to a sign on the wall: NO MOBILE PHONES ON FACTORY FLOOR.

As a follow-up tactic, he also points to your ribcage, except this time using a sword rather than a finger and using an attacking motion rather than a point. As the last vestiges of life drain from your body, the last things you see are feathery hands putting you into a rubber coffin and throwing you into a kiln.

Your adventure ends here.

52

Warily you continue down the corridor and push through the double doors into a busy open-plan office. You can scarce believe your eyes.

Small winged creatures flit over filing cabinets, elves chatter into headsets, and an enchanted swan rocks back on a swivel chair, hissing industriously. Wraiths coo maternally round a kobold's baby while a pool of gnomes type documents effectively and rapidly in the centre of the room.

You stand aghast at the fantastical abominations until a dwarf on an office scooter knocks you out of the way.

In the midst of this madness a kindly voice booms behind you, 'Well met, colleague.'

You turn to see a man in a short-sleeved shirt standing behind a counter. Relieved to see one of your own kind, you rush eagerly to greet the man, who steps out from behind his counter, revealing monstrous hindquarters.

You collapse at the hooves of a centaur.

Turn to **193**.

53

Finishing up your lunch, you pull out the buzzard to see if it has survived the torrid temperatures stifled inside your cloak.

As soon as its head emerges, it delivers an almighty

'SCRAAAAAAA!' and pecks violently at your fingers, lips and ears.

The phoenixes utter a collective 'Aaaah!' and start cooing over it like a coachload of hot feathery aunts.

'Whose-a-liddle-lovely? Whose-a-lovely-liddle-thing? Eh? Eh?'

The buzzard laps up the attention and chirps happily while being tickled under the chin. A clucky phoenix tells you that it has your beak but its mother's craw.

You need to try and find some djinn tears but— Yes, he is lovely, isn't he? These djinn tears – do any of you ladies know where— Yes, a real cutie-pie. Does anyone know where— Mainly mice, but he still likes his rusks too.

You can't get any sense out of the broody birds and to cap it all they call over their manager to come and have a look at your buzzard. Hang on! That manager is . . . a djinn!

Turn to **156**.

54

You are about to plan your television schedule for the night when, with a shriek of horror, you look over your shoulder to see that your shirt is ripped to pieces and you're bleeding to death from a gaping cut.

You cry out in agony for someone to help you, but get distracted halfway through by a poster showing a chimp in a sideways baseball cap. This really tickles you and, as a result, your yelp comes out 'HELLL-ha-ha-ha!'

You sink to the ground, writhing in pain and humour. As the last vestiges of life drain from your body, a tea lady in a tabard leans over your cubicle wall and points at the poster with a chuckle.

'Hee hee! That's an absolute riot, isn't it?'

Your adventure ends here.

55

The Kraken's tentacles wind around the ship, covering all the main areas. Bow tentacle? Check. Stern tentacle? Check. Mast tentacle? Oh yeah.

The timbers of the deck groan but, despite covering all the main areas, the Kraken cannot get a real purchase and the ship slips through its suckers like soap in a bath.

As the *Golden Scart* rocks wildly in the ocean, crew members scatter in a blind panic and a terrified sea trog gets the willies right in front of you.

When next it rears up, the Kraken's barnacle-encrusted tentacles deftly grab maritime office workers, pulling their heads and legs off as if it was eating unshelled prawns. It gulps down a hobgoblin whole like an oyster.

Shaking with fear, you help a sea dwarf aim a mighty cannon at the Kraken's slick translucent hide. In your desperation to kill the beast, you accidentally fire too early and shoot the dwarf off the ship with a cannonball. You manage to see the dwarf's startled disappointment before the Kraken sucks him out of the sea like a beardy crouton.

You flee the scene but trip on a pair of smoking dwarfish deck shoes and gain 1 Splinter in Your Thumb.

Eventually the mighty Kraken manages to get some purchase on the ship and crushes it to pieces before sinking down to the black depths from which it came, taking an admin cabin boy as a travel snack.

You are left clinging perilously to a piece of flotsam with a sea gnome. The gnome bagsies the good end of the flotsam and you exchange sharp words.

The rest of your days are spent floating in mutual angry silence on a piece of flotsam until you die of septicaemia from an untreated splinter.

56

Your supernaturally extended neck is clearly a must-have item for the headhunter, who yells, 'Need bad!' and begins a curious barefoot dance.

The dance is a kind of hornpipe which incorporates moves of Michael Jackson's 'Thriller', namely the 'claw sweep' and the 'dead-man's crick'.

Suddenly your head emits an embarrassing *peeeeee-wit!* sound and shrinks to the size of a golfball.

Your adventure, as well as your days of trying on hats that you never intend to buy, ends here.

57

While washing your hands, you notice a bulky vending machine in the corner of the room. The sign on the machine reads RIDDLE VEND. It is obviously some cheap staff perk but you are intrigued none the less and decide to investigate.

You press the only button on the machine and a parchment drops on to the floor at your feet. You pick it up and read the following:

> *My first is in buzzard but never in mire,*
> *My second is in buzzard but not forest fire,*
> *My third is in buzzard and also in pez,*
> *My fourth the last letter of the alphabet,*
> *My fifth is in buzzard and also in dream,*
> *The sixth of my letters in buzzard is seen,*
> *My last is in dandy and also in dird.*
> *Yet what is the name of this carrion bird?*

Solve the riddle by adding up the letters in your answer, valued at their corresponding place in the alphabet, e.g. a=1, b=2, c=3 etc., then turn to that section.

'Buzzard', for example, would be 2+21+26+26+1+18+4 = 98, so you would turn to **98**.

If you cannot solve the vended riddle, just chuck the parchment into a toilet, head back to your desk and turn to **173**.

58

You miss the bin badly but cover it up by telling the treefolk that THAT is what you think of their faun boss!

Almost instantly, after about forty minutes, the dander of the trees is well and truly up and they all follow suit, throwing their paperwork on to the floor, narrowly missing bins with revolutionary zeal.

'Now follow me!' you cry.

Some of the treefolk wail that you are speaking too fast, but most are right behind you. Within hours, the lynch-mob of lumber marches on Faun Ditter just as he is about to leave for the day. You can't rely on your monotonous militia, so you must fight . . . ALONE!

FAUN DITTER   APTITUDE 2   ENDURANCE 1

If you dispose of Ditter, turn to **23**.

59

Pressing on, you return to the open-plan office staffed with the creatures of legend.

It's business as usual, except the tea lady in a tabard is struggling to push the Aztec-looking portal on castors, while the IT troll with a mobile phone in a leather pouch attached to its wrist looks on.

A griffin is introducing himself as the new head of IHR to the other staff, while a magic chimp flits after him, trying to take his measurements.

Things move fast round here.

Turn to **257**.

60

Remembering the maxim 'Attack is the best form of attack,' you punch the headhunter squarely in the golden nose-bone! The headhunter stumbles and falls mouth-first against a dusty shelf.

Pierced eyes watering, he advances furiously on YOU!

HEADHUNTER   APTITUDE 32   ENDURANCE 31

If you defeat the headhunter, turn to **132**.

61

Your common type-A blood sizzles in the Portal, which burns brighter for an instant as a huge sub-bass *whump!* sound shakes through the room.

The room is darkened with shadow and someone at the back goes, 'Oh my days.'

Filling the entire room is the biggest dragon you have *ever* seen.

Because you summoned it, the dragon will fight the mob on your behalf! Should it be slain, YOU must step in yourself.

BIG FUCK-OFF
DRAGON   APTITUDE 12   ENDURANCE 50

vs

ENTIRE STAFF OF
LOWER ADMIN   APTITUDE 3   ENDURANCE 87

Should you or your dragon prevent the advance of lower admin, turn to **26**.

62

You come face to face to face to face to face with a many-headed giant serpent gleaming like oil in the torchlight.

So busy are the heads gospering* that it's a while before you're noticed, which gives you time to take in the horrifying scene.

Tangled in the coils of the beast's underbelly, you spy something gleaming. With a leap of your heart, you see the brass hoops of a lever-arch file glinting under the panel lighting. The spine of the file is engraved with a number. And that number is . . . One.

Turn to **172**.

> *gospering: *the act of blatantly discussing an issue or person in a low voice in front of an outsider who isn't meant to hear. The outsider feels like less than nothing.*

63

You pick up the phone and bark at the receptionist to stop sending aggressive PAs up to you. But it is not the receptionist on the other end!

Instead of the receptionist's incandescent tones, you are treated to an earful of abuse from the head of filing, complaining about your lower admin staff filing their work in the filing.

This doesn't make any sense at all.

The head of filing informs you that he's now replaced the One File in the Labyrinth Department so proper filing can be done again.

Unable to fathom the head of filing's file ramblings,

you simply hang up and head over to a nearby water cooler, desperate to avoid your relentlessly ringing phone.

Turn to **16**.

64

You begin scribbling down notes about how best to retrieve the One File when the phone rings at your desk.

Answering, you hear an albino voice on the other end saying, 'First candidate for your PA cover is here.' You tell the receptionist to hold them for a minute but there is already a knock at the door!

Within seconds you are shaking the hand of an imp and asking if he's 'come far'. The imp doesn't answer but instead draws a glyph in the air with a warty finger. It could be a religious custom so you let it go.

If the Wurst Witch bestowed the Curse of Wits on you, turn to **153**.

If the Wurst Witch did not bestow the Curse of Wits on you, turn to **180**.

65

You descend at a gentle rate and come to a plain wooden door. There's nothing else to do round here so you go through it.

Turn to **100**.

66

Holding the sack, you ask the centaur how his human heart manages to pump an extra eighty litres of blood round the horse part of his body. The centaur shrugs and keeps franking mail.

You then ask the centaur if he has two bowels and when he empties them which toilets does he use. The centaur shrugs again.

Then you ask the centaur how he manages stairs and he informs you he takes the lift. Then you ask the centaur if, when he takes the lift, he counts as two people or one, to which the centaur shrugs.

Then you absent-mindedly pat the centaur's buttocks and study his form, which turns out to be the last straw.

'Enough! You have insulted the majesty of the centaur for the last time!'

It seems you have unwittingly upset a colleague and must fight . . . to the death!

POST-ROOM CENTAUR   APTITUDE 10   ENDURANCE 15

If you defeat him turn to **235**.

Otherwise, your adventure ends here.

67

ˊɳdɣ ɕƂɒb ɕ ccɅɒ

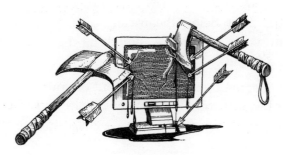

68

A middle-management faun marches in and obnoxiously tells everyone to get back to work 'chop-chop', a phrase that causes the whole office to shiver their timbers.

From behind a cold-calling coppice, you study the naggingly familiar faun. It looks a lot like Bernie Ditter but wearing hairy trousers and with half-coconut shells over his brogues to make them look like hooves. You have no hesitation in agreeing to subdue the pseudo-satyr.

Not having had a proper lunch, you feel weak and decide a mass-attack would be the safest option. You must now attempt to raise the fury of the treefolk.

Test your luck! Screw some scrap paper into a ball (the publisher's copyright page at the front of this book will do), then throw it at a bin at least four metres away.

If you get it into the bin, turn to **204**.

If you miss the bin, turn to **58**.

Note to reader: No 'best of three's.

69

Exhausted after being theatrically sick, you lie face-down in your hammock, breathing heavily, badly needing a friend.

As if on cue, the buzzard bustles out of your cloak and cocks its head at you.

You go to pet it but the ship lurches and you are theatrically sick again.

Then the buzzard takes a nip at you.

With all the strength you can muster, you hit the buzzard and tell it 'fuck off'. It flaps to the other side of the sick bay, irritated to have pecked too soon.

Strength well and truly sapped, you spend your last days batting away a buzzard who loiters like a busy mother at a microwave, waiting for you to ping. Your adventure ends here.

70

You snatch up the phone, saying, 'Good afternoon, Firetop Mountain?' into the receiver.

'Hooooom,' says a really slow voice on the other end. 'Is . . . it . . . afternoon . . . already?'

'Sorry, good morning,' you reply tetchily, realizing it's still before 12 p.m.

'Wishing . . . the . . . day . . . away . . . are . . . we?'

The voice laughs into the receiver for far too long. The caller is being suspiciously friendly and you realize you're dealing with a sales call from someone with a really slow voice. Lose . . . 2 . . . ENDURANCE . . . points.

From behind you, a sound like someone quickly assembling a xylophone breaks you out of your trance.

Turn to **267**.

71

You look over your shoulder, to find your worst fears confirmed.

A gaping rent has been cut into your back! Dark red blood pumps lazily over a sinister blade glinting in the seat of your chair!

Ice cold with terror, you jump up and pratfall backwards in a slick of your own blood, which is flowing towards the concrete gutter below.

With no warning, the lights are extinguished and the computer screens go blank, making a *DOOoooooooo* sound as they power down!

In the total blackout you hear strange cries, footsteps running back and forth and . . . is that the sound of hooves?

You must get out. You must get out.

Will you flee to the left (**219**)?

Or to the right (**122**)?

72

The uncollected document appears to be a poorly drafted romance novel set under a bridge, called *Forbidden Lace*. Someone has clearly been wasting company paper printing out their own creative writing.

You flick through the draft but the font is so large that it reads like an optometrist's wallchart and you have to cover one eye to make out the raunchy bits. You are so absorbed in the terrible novel that you all but fail to hear the sound of an approaching co-worker!

Turn to **82**.

73

Every creature has its weapon drawn on you as you stand in a silence broken only by the bleating of a lamb.

A hideous goblin steps forth with a javelin. Everyone waits for it to speak.

'Are you off your head?' says the goblin in a really high voice.

'You've picked on that lamb,' says something else.

Everyone looks daggers at you. Then someone throws daggers at you.

Finally, a griffin smacks you in the chops with a wireless keyboard and calls you a ponce.

Your adventure ends here.

74

Girding your loins for the data entry ahead, your trembling thumb presses the 240V button. An electric shock courses through your arm! It's agony! It must be at least 240 volts. Possibly a bit more!

Throw a dice to determine your OFFICE LUCK. If you throw lower than a 4, there is a history of heart disease in your family and your adventure ends here.

If you throw a 4 or above, you're as strong as an ox and you soak up the electrocution without breaking a sweat. Feeling energized and ready for the day ahead, you press the button marked RECEPTION.

Turn to **184**.

75

You clamber out of the lake, noticing you are still holding the pink holepunch! A power-dressed merman bursts to the surface and attempts to chase you down the corridor but the fish in him lets him down.

Once safe, you examine the holepunch closely, realizing it to be an awful, awful treasure that will never be of use.

You sludge miserably up the corridor towards the warmth of the candy-cane trees. Passing the motivational penguin poster you replace the word COURAGE with BASTARD.

Turn to **6**.

Before you can react, the sphinx intones her riddle . . . at YOU!

> *What am I?*
> *I can visit at night*
> *Or arrive in the day,*
> *I will always remain*
> *Even once I'm away.*
> *I will make all men poorer*
> *And cause health to fray.*
> *Yet if you catch me in your house it*
> *is* technically illegal *to assault me.*
> *What am I?*

If you work out the riddle, add up the numbers of the letters as before. 'Burglar', for example, would be 2+21+18+7+12+1+18 = **79**.

You bat the shapeshifter's appendages away, yet it won't take no for an answer and advances on you as a spinning rack of saucy seaside postcards.

Turning into a tongue, it insists you choose a family member to see in the nude!

You draw your sword against the wretch. A thick hush fills the room. Lizard bowmen cock their arrows; halflings rest their sword arms on their dirks. A cockatrice pats its beak menacingly.

'THIS CREATURE IS AN ABOMINATION!' you yell, outraged at the general reaction. 'It has come into my space and harassed me and I have been defiled!'

Then you turn to see that the shapeshifter has become a demure lamb, bleating sorrowfully at everyone in the room.

Test your luck!

If you roll equal or greater than your OFFICE LUCK score, turn to 13.

If you roll less than your OFFICE LUCK score, turn to 73.

78

You begin to realize now how that Minotaur ended up getting lost. Keep on trudging.

Turn to 106.

79

'I am a burglar!' you cry, and the sphinx bobs her head mechanically.

'So are you answering the riddle or just telling me you're a burglar?' she queries.

You declare the former (unless in real life you are a burglar, in which case you are a bastard).

The sphinx rears up on her haunches. 'Very well, you may pass,' she roars. 'After ANOTHER RIDDLE, that is!'

You bluster in protest but she has already begun a new riddle, this time with *multiple choices*!

> *What walks on two legs in the afternoon, twenty legs in the evening and ninety legs at night?*

Do you answer:

A) The three ages of man (**197**)?

B) A robin standing on a caterpillar which ends up standing on a centipede (**147**)?

C) A really successful conga (**255**)?

80

You begin to suspect that adventuring down that sloping ramp was a bad decision.

Turn to **29**.

81

You arrive at a vast stone door with the words ONE FILE ROOM chiselled deep into the living rock. Guarding the door is a giant recumbent lioness with a handsome human head.

This zoomorphic creature senses your presence and rears up awkwardly like an animatronic dinosaur at a theme park.

'I am Sphinx 4.2,' croaks the sphinx, 'copyright 2000 BC.'

You are about to push open the huge stone door when a paw the size of a camper van lands in your path.

'All who would enter the One File room must answer the riddle with which I will charge!' she continues, then adds, in an entirely different and quite perky voice, 'Updates are ready to install.'

Do you have a gorgon's head? If so, turn to **218**.

If not, turn to **76**.

82

Adrenalin starts pumping as you look nervously up the tunnel and make out the unmistakable shadow of a photocopier-repair gorgon advancing towards you! If she decides to fight you, the chances are you'll be done for. Thinking quickly, you scribble OUT OF ORDER on a piece of paper and pop it on top of the photocopier, hoping this will distract the gorgon's attention long enough for you to make your escape.

Disaster! The tunnel is too breezy for the message to stay put! You grab for some nearby sticky tape to fix the message to the copier.

Turn to **241**.

83

Your offer of nuts and berries is received badly by the hounds. The slavering stock takers howl and chase their tails like they've got the rips. Trying to bring them to heel is impossible. They're being BAD dogs. BAD dogs. That's right, you are NAUGHTY dogs. Sit! Sit!

But the feral auditors won't sit. With angry paws the pack advances . . . on you!

FERAL AUDITORS   APTITUDE 6   ENDURANCE 11

If you defeat the feral auditors, turn to **46**.

84

You manage to get your out-of-order diversion to stick to the copier just as the gorgon slithers towards you. Her perishing gaze fixes immediately on the sign, not on you, and in a voice like an angry goose she hisses something about toner.

While the gorgon bends over to investigate paper tray 3, you realize you could render the swarthy beast unconscious with a mighty shoe.

Now throw a shoe at an object roughly the size of a swarthy gorgon's head.

If you hit, turn to **230**.

If you miss, turn to **143**.

85

You head below deck, past the high elf, who tells you he's waiting for an urgent pirate fax.

You open the salt-encrusted door and enter a dark cabin with a clear nautical theme. At a driftwood desk a fire sprite is writing industriously in a Red and Black note pad. The fire sprite is not best suited to sea travel and is waxy as a result.

As you approach, the sprite jerks its head up.

'So many accidents when you're in the middle of a hostile takeover,' it confides to you nervously.

You peer down and see that the fire sprite's notebook is headed ACCIDENT BOOK. Hiding your excitement, you tell a big lie that you are a director of Firetop Mountain and must have the accident book at once.

'All directors are attending a crisis meeting about the hostile takeover in Meeting Cabin A. Why aren't you there?' queries the fire sprite, jabbing you in the chest with a hot pen.

You are about to bluster your way out of this when the cabin lurches and a wave of nausea crashes over you. Not yet having your sea legs, you begin to feel very ill!

Turn to **146**.

86

The heat is blistering but, by focusing on how easy-going your friends are, you manage to pull through.

In fact, now you've got a good sweat on, the heat is really quite pleasant. Like being on holiday, say.

Looking visibly relaxed, you begin to think about lunch. Possibly a Spanish omelette and some sangria.

Turn to **32**.

87

With much trepidation, you push open the red door and step into a fiery sweatshop as hot as a kiln. Armoured trolls work at anvils, pounding holepunch teeth from pig-iron. Steam mixes with smoke. Condensation pours in rivers down the walls.

You walk past the deafening clang towards a row of phoenixes in tabards sitting at sewing machines and nattering away to each other. They sew like their lives depend on it, examining each stitch with desperate beady eyes. As you approach, a noticeably mangy phoenix screams:

'I CAN'T . . . TAKE . . . ANY . . . MORE . . . SEWING!'

Woooooooof! She bursts into flames, causing even the trolls to stop their hammering and stare.

Wide-eyed you watch as, from the phoenix's smouldering remains, a baby phoenix emerges, stinking like an ashtray.

'Aaaaah,' says a clucky phoenix. 'Did you have a good break, Val?'

'Ee, it were cracking!' says the baby phoenix, 'but I feel like I were never away now I'm back.'

'Tell me about it,' says the clucky phoenix, adding, 'Still, only eighty-seven years till the next one.'

'And counting!' says the baby phoenix, picking up where she left off.

Turn to **151**.

88

You find the photocopier at the end of a long corridor next to a gaping stone doorway, through which blows a warm breeze like a hairdryer on low. Around the photocopier are a collection of statues of blue-collar elves and orcs in various states of alarm.

You don't much care for modern interior design, so you ignore the statues, set the copier to 'Staple: collate' and ponder how to enter the Labyrinth Department undetected.

While concocting a plan of action, you notice a large document sitting uncollected in the printer tray. You are about to investigate when you hear a sound like someone yelling, and then ice cubes cracking as they drop into a warm liquid.

To investigate the stack of papers, turn to **72**.

To investigate the curious sound, turn to **82**.

89

The Wurst Witch howls a death rattle.

'Eeeeeee, my lardy victor! You may have won the battle but you have also won a curse!' she screeches, pointing to a wall of sausage sea scrolls. 'Anything on the middle row, between the plague of locusts and the angry bowel!'

You have seconds to decide on the nature of your curse.

To choose the Curse of the Long Neck, turn to **271**.

To choose the Curse of Promotion, turn to **160**.

90

The Minotaur falls against a stack of chairs, smashing its face and breaking an ankle on the way down. Using quips as a coping mechanism, you say something about 'foot and mouth' before 'taking the bull by the horns' and dragging it out of the 'way in a manger'. You also try to do something with 'cattle grid' but it doesn't come off.

Fired up after your rodeo-style ruck, you hear the sound of raucous laughter coming from what looks to be an abandoned HR department at the end of the corridor.

Moving close to the door, you ascertain that it is in fact possibly 'orcish laughter' you can hear. With no other option you decide to investigate.

Will you burst in unannounced (**110**)?

Knock and wait (**205**)?

Or knock and go straight in (**11**)?

91

You are glad to be leaving the slow-paced sales spinney. As you trek out of the office and retrace your steps to the green door you hear the loud report of a sales bell being rung over the forest.

The sound upsets a stork, causing it to burst high above the forest in a shower of falling leaves.

Turn to **174**.

92

Leaving your sword and straining against a remarkably strong magnet, you use a clever body-rotation system to lurch across the floor with the metal file.

You are halfway to the painted wall when two halflings on a conference call drop their phones and rush at you!

You believe the game to be up, but the halflings misinterpret your urgent hunched rotation to be a dance from The Shire and join in.

This creates an excellent diversion and you manage to lug the One File through the painted wall as the griffin has a stern word with two rotating halflings.

Turn to **232**.

93

You chat to Jessie as if small-talk were your mother tongue. Gain 1 APTITUDE point!

Within the space of five minutes you cover:

- bodies of water
- what you'd do if you won the Lottery
- what you'd do if zombies took over the world
- snakes
- the dream packed lunch

Smiling good-naturedly, you sit back down. After ten minutes of staring at you, Jessie says, 'See you at lunch!' and his precariously supported head disappears from view into his own cubicle.

Turn to **18**.

94

Smugly praising your foresight for never having cloaked a wretched buzzard, and with nothing else to encumber your progress, you pick up the hessian sack and venture gingerly through the door into the mysterious Labyrinth Department!

Turn to **210**.

95

You sit down on a wooden sofa, which is more comfortable than it sounds, but not as comfortable as it looks. After a few minutes, a thin man limps into the room on an orthopaedic shoe and introduces himself as Bernie Ditter. He has an angry bloodshot eye and brings with him the odour of death.

Bernie Ditter asks about your office experience and makes a tick on a heavy wooden clipboard as you answer, all the time rubbing his ruby-red eye.

He explains that, rub-rub, you have an arduous data-entry task ahead of you, rub-rub. No one minds if, rub-rub, you check your email every now and, rub-rub, then. But, rub-rub, please save your work, rub-rub, regularly, rub, and get someone to, rub-rub, check it before you leave. Rub.

Bernie Ditter's eye is now redder than Hades itself, so it is with much trepidation that you follow him into an open-plan office, noticing that his clipboard holds one blank sheet of A4 with a single biro tick on it.

Turn to **22**.

96

You hold the head of the gorgon up at the mighty sphinx.

'Whoah! That thing should be on a lead,' remarks the sphinx sarcastically, batting it unconscious into the shadows.

This was not the outcome you had hoped for.

'Now, about that riddle . . .' says the sphinx.

Turn to **76**.

97

The eagle dies quickly and its carcass takes up most of the office. Spitting feathers, you try to order a cup of tea on the intercom before remembering that you *still* have no PA. You gaze wistfully at the gently rotting eagle and sigh for things that might have been – like the cup of tea it might have made you.

Aside from a cockatrice being sexually harassed by a shapeshifter outside your window, the next hours pass without incident.

Still thirsty, you contemplate stealing a cup of tea from someone else's desk when your computer makes a *boop* noise to alert you that an email has arrived. In a heart-beat, the phone starts ringing! AGAIN! You now face exactly the sort of decision top-brass management are paid extra to deal with.

To read the email, turn to **104**.

To answer the phone, turn to **63**.

98

Adeptly solving the riddle, you say the word 'buzzard' out loud.

The vending machine makes one loud CLUNK and a hatch at floor level opens, letting a buzzard waddle slowly out.

You stare at the buzzard. The buzzard stares back. Given the magnitude of everything you've had to take in, it is somewhat underwhelming. In fact, you could argue that this buzzard-dispensing riddle machine is wasted on you right now.

To discard the buzzard in a toilet, turn to **183**.

To keep the buzzard in the folds of your cloak, turn to **260**.

99

Instantly you lop the gold head off the hydra, which takes the other heads by surprise.

'You really should have made an appointment if you wanted to attack,' says the flustered azure head.

'Actually I think I can fit an attack in,' says the green head. 'TGIF is what I say.'

The hydra's green head rears up and sighs spitty acid at you. It's a snaky scrap . . . to the death!

GREEN HEAD   APTITUDE **12**   ENDURANCE **8**

If you defeat the green head, the white head says, 'Were you waiting *very* long?' and attacks.

WHITE HEAD   APTITUDE **12**   ENDURANCE **8**

If you defeat the white head, you notice two heads re-form on the gold head's stump.

The black head then starts talking them through the handover, stating that you are an ongoing task.

It's hydra heads a-gogo from now on in.

If at any time you wish to step off this magic reptilian jobshare roundabout, turn to **202**.

100

You're in a black tunnel with walls and a ceiling. You go along it.

Turn to **162**.

101

The Kraken rears up a full thirty storeys, causing the ship to almost capsize. The crew buggers about in a blind panic as the Kraken picks them off like a guest at a seafood wedding buffet. Like most guests, it appears to be here for the food more than the occasion.

Salt waves crash over the ship, and you see the fire sprite darting around the deck recording the death toll in the accident book, all the time whingeing that it can't keep up with the paperwork.

You consider splashing the sprite to death for the book when the buzzard forces its way out of your cloak and flies at the Kraken's head.

While biting the head off a dosser, the Kraken irritably bats the buzzard, screeching at it like a drunk bride.

Without warning, the buzzard stupidly flies into the Kraken's mouth and gets stuck in its craw. Breathlessly the Kraken tries to beat its own back before collapsing into the sea with eyes the size of ice-cream vans gawking out of its monster skull.

Kabloooooooooosh!

Waves crash over the side of the ship and the accident book washes up against your feet. The sea is a fickle mistress indeed! The surviving crew look over the ship's stern and coo at the ripples the Kraken made.

As you pick up the accident book, you hear the captain lament, ''Twas a buzzard killed the beast.'

Turn to 12.

102

You stand eye to beak with a parrot office manager who says, 'What can I do you for?', *not* for the first time that day.

You explain that you have been sent to collect the accident book of the office ship, but the parrot just ruffles its chest and ignores you.

To ignore the parrot and find other crew members to quiz, turn to 248.

To ask again, turn to 102.

103

You walk further down the tunnel.

Turn to 42.

104

Ignoring that incessantly ringing phone, which was probably only a call from the glow-in-the-dark receptionist, you open your email and immediately feel like someone is shouting in your face. It reads:

GREETINGS! I AM A MIGHTY DJINN! YOU HAVE BEEN CHOSEN TO HAVE THREE WISHES GRANTED! THE THREE WISHES CHOSEN FOR YOU ARE:

1 UNTOLD RICHES

2 A MIGHTY MANHOOD

3 CHEAP VIAGRA

TO CLAIM YOUR THREE WISHES, SEND YOUR BANK ACCOUNT DETAILS TO:
MIGHTYDJINN@BANKOFDJINN.COM!

TO UNSUBSCRIBE FROM THIS EMAIL, SEND YOUR BANK ACCOUNT DETAILS TO:
MIGHTYDJINN@BANKOFDJINN.COM!

The Mighty Djinn's email has greatly sapped your energy. Lose 1 ENDURANCE point. With a heart still racing from all the exclamation marks and capital letters, you delete the email then head over to the water cooler to replenish your strength.

Turn to **16**.

105

You approach the smokers, who shuffle up to make room for you, and a pixie crashes you a snout.

Lighting your cigarette, you feel the welcome rush of pleasure that non-smokers probably feel all the time.

A sea trog throws his fag into the sea and heads back on to the ship. You shift up for a pirate monkey, who lights up two for kicks. A harpy arrives with her baccy and a half elf shuffles along tooting on a briar pipe.

The pixie flutters back to work muttering something about a 'hostile takeover', leaving you at the end of the plank.

Then a halfling shows up with a giant clay bong and you feel yourself teeter on the ledge. Suddenly you topple backwards!

You have inadvertently walked the smokers' plank!

AH-HAAAAAAAR!

Down you go into the icy briny.

Your adventure is extinguished here.

106

You see a magnet on the floor but are so bored you leave it. You walk on and think about the magnet in time with your footsteps: Mag. Net. Mag. Net. Mag. Net. On you lumber.

Turn to 279.

107

Have you cloaked a buzzard?

Nuh uh (199)?

Yuh huh (69)?

108

You return to find the hydra is listening to five different language cassettes, repeating phrases like 'Where is the garage?' in various tongues.

The djinn tears have frozen solid in the mould, due to the sharp drop in room temperature. You rattle them in the mould, which gets the hydra's undivided attention.

The hydra reverently places the One File in your grasp.

The brass bolts are cool . . . steady . . . and brassy.

At last you will be able to face the Regional Accounts Director.

At last you will have revenge.

Turn to **27**.

109

It hurts to do so but you release the buzzard. The buzzard is not for you. The buzzard is no longer a keeper.

As you abandon him by the photocopier, he gawks and leers in a way that breaks your heart. You will always remember this moment the two of you shared together. Your tears fall like rain on the ground.

Heavy-hearted and with a heavy head in a hessian bag, you head through the door into the sinister Labyrinth Department!

Turn to **210**.

110

As you enter the room the first thing that hits you is a Frisbee of carpet, right in the face.

The next thing that hits you is the smell, then the heat, then the graze from the carpet Frisbee. Lose 2 ENDURANCE points.

Two orcs, one tall and one stout, look sheepishly at you as you notice a circle has been cut out from the carpet near the doorway. You've clearly interrupted the two orcs in their Frisbee game.

The tall orc halts and says, 'Ftuooh nach laxangst?', straightening his ginger war-braids.

You shake your head in confusion.

'Then be thankful we have learned the common tongue of man!' bellows the stout orc, and bowls towards you with a stout sword!

Turn to **49**.

111

The elf moves towards you.

Fortunately the cheese from the pizza has sealed his eyelids closed.

Unfortunately he can see a bit through one cheesy eye.

Fortunately the elf is not on duty and so does not tazer you.

Unfortunately his colleague behind you *is* on duty and tazers you into the middle of next week.

Fortunately you collapse with impressive dignity.

Unfortunately you kneel on a pencil, which hurts.

Fortunately the pencil wound is not fatal.

Unfortunately the sharp teeth of a merman returning from a dip in the staff pool are fatal.

Fortunately you enjoy being a ghost.

Unfortunately other ghosts talk about you behind your back.

Fortunately the other ghosts talk about what a nice ghost you are.

Your adventure ends here.

112

Feeling the refracted gaze of mermen on you, you waft hesitantly in the water. They can smell your fear!

'Behold an office coward!' says the nearest, advancing on you with the holepunch.

Pank! You are hit in the head by a corporate trident.

Test your luck!

> If you roll less than your OFFICE LUCK score, turn to **211**.
>
> If you roll more, turn to **195**.

113

Your gut reaction is to forget about this stupid quest and skip straight to the fabulously wealthy part of your life, so you wish for untold riches.

Within moments, you are wearing a crown and all your clothes are made of gold – even your scarf. Surrounding you now are donkeys as far as the eye can see, all laden with treasures and trained to follow wherever you go.

A flood of joy washes through you with the realization that you will never have to work as a temp again.

'That is *just* the tonic,' you sigh, as the stresses and strains of a working life leave your body for ever.

'Oh you cheap, cheap sod,' spits the djinn and runs you through with a poisoned scimitar before a single donkey can canter to your defence.

Your adventure ends here.

114

What a stink!

The syrupy subterfuge has mixed with the processed meat and the whole room smells like an American's breakfast.

You open a small ham window to let out the stench and carefully examine the witch's office.

Your eyes fall on the sausage key. Eagerly you try it in the cabinet!

Aside from a tiny doll's-house office populated with little workers, nothing interests you. You eat the key in boredom and immediately gain 5 ENDURANCE points – magically healing the cut in your back!

But wait.

Your eyes fall on two cloaks, one grey, one bottle green. The former has OFFICE JUNIOR roughly sewn into the hem, while the latter is embroidered with MIDDLE MANAGEMENT.

It seems you have a choice of position on this floor. You can hide in the shadows of lower admin (**50**).

Or fake it on the throne of top brass (**129**).

115

When you get back the hydra is receiving a formal

verbal warning from a sand fairy which is embarrassing to watch.

You throw the sea-sodden accident book down in front of it.

The hydra sniffs and passes you the One File with the reverence of the very recently bollocked.

You hold the One File in your hands. Compared to the accident book, it's really dry.

At last you will be able to face the Regional Accounts Director.

At last you will have revenge.

Turn to **27**.

116

Slinnk hits a dimmer switch and holds a torch to the underside of his face, looking at you gravely.

'*I gador prestar aen*. The office is changed. I feel it in the water. I feel it in the earth.

'For many an age, our people lived in war-like idyll with other races not of your world. Our status quo was hatred and death. Many was the time that Orom and I would feast on elf flesh and befoul the clean waters of rivers with our behinds.

'This was before the coming of the accountant. In this world he is known as the Regional Accounts Director. A man who walked among us, speaking of regular pay. The rewards were high, but he demanded sacrifices: a strict dress policy and seven-day weeks without a single duvet day in sight.

'The races of our world were furious. None of us wanted jobs in the first place. There was a wailing and gnashing of teeth which could be heard at the peaks of the Black Mountains of Hrggn U-oth. Fires raged for days and a coalition of races formed to defeat this fiscal reaper on the plains of Barroo.

'We were prepared for war but we were not prepared for the accountant's weapon. He met us on the field of war with a strange device – a portal. As our gathered armies advanced to attack, he cast spells of employment which were contractually binding.

'Fuelled by the blood of human temps, the Portal ripped us from our world and brought us into yours. We remain shackled here until the day when the spell is cast that reverses the Portal.

'Yet alack the spell is hidden in a black lever-arch file. A file forged by the hands of man: the One File.

'A file which archives our ensnarement and so holds the key to freedom.

> *'One file to keep receipts,*
> *One file to file them,*
> *One file to list deceits*
> *And in A4 photo-quality lamination bind them.*

'Our lives are worth naught here. We have not tasted elf flesh for months. Most of them have good offices on the upper floors where we are not allowed.'

Turn to **163**.

117

You knock boldly on the door and a slick velvet voice calls, 'Come in!'

Still feeling a bit windy, you creep cautiously into an antique room containing a leathery desk and a portal on wheels.

At the desk is a man with a stance that would strike fear into anyone, causing them to let off. But having just seen his portrait, you remain icy calm. Gain 2 APTITUDE points.

In a pin-striped power robe, the Regional Accounts Director allows his white eyes to bore into you and he steeples his ice-white fingers with nails like manicured nails – the other kind of nails though.

'So you are the temp who's been creating all the vacancies,' he jests icily, producing your timesheet! 'You'll need this signed, then . . . I'll put you down for twenty hours . . . since you've clearly been so busy today.'

He signs it with an elaborate quill and mockingly holds it out to you.

As if you're playing a corporate version of paper-scissors-stone you produce the One File. The accountant's grin evaporates.

'My dear, I'm going to do something I never do now, and that is to give one of my workers a choice.' As he grins you swear you see pointed teeth. 'You can either hear all about me and that folder you hold . . . or be slain where you stand.'

To play for time and hear your arch-enemy's back-story, turn to **220**.

To face the dread fiscal reaper now, turn to **28**.

118

You pass the interview with flying colours and the imp shakes your hand vigorously while congratulating you on getting the job. In a confusing exchange, you then tell the imp that the PA job he came for has already been filled, and he sulks out of the office.

Still bewildered from the imp glyph, you then issue yourself a formal warning for interviewing candidates for a job that had been filled. Lose 2 APTITUDE points.

You are about to ask yourself if you want a cup of tea when a giant eagle bursts into the room, clutching a CV in one of its bony claws. You try to tell it that the PA vacancy has been filled but the eagle wants a proper interview! Your only option is to expound your experience . . . as a fighter!

GIANT EAGLE   APTITUDE 8   ENDURANCE 14

If you defeated the typist's talons, turn to **97**.

119

The lift is as slow as a cloud.

The wizards clearly know each other but your presence is holding them back from chatting. It gets so bad that you consider snapping one of your fingers off to break the silent tension.

After a while the paler one mutters to his colleague, 'I made a few ales disappear last night.'

The other wizard snorts with derisive laughter. Then nothing.

'I was out with that Snow Witch again . . .'

'Oooh,' says the other. 'Did you trouble it?'

The first wizard makes a hand gesture you don't understand but it looks sordid or tacky, possibly both.

You wince with embarrassment as the lift continues its maddeningly slow ascent.

Turn to **48**.

120

With the skeleton staff out of the way, you turn back to the data entry.

The morning passes completely without incident, aside from a giant eagle ripping the manager's office to shreds. Then a flibbertigibbet sings mournfully about the dank caves of home and a nak weeps into its Lilt. None of these creatures belongs here.

With clenched fists you search the room for some clue about the One File to free these enslaved beasts, when a gossamer hand brushes your neck. You turn to see a beautiful elf patting you in a way that's right for you.

Then the gossamer hand becomes a leeching tentacle and you recoil instantly.

Where the elf stood is now some kind of perverse octopus which humps the air with an erect tentacle while going, 'PWHOAR!'

You are being sexually harassed by a shapeshifter!

Instantly you feel a fiery rage in your belly, yet you realize that making a scene could blow your cover.

Will you confront this erotic terror (**77**)?

Or put up with the pest (**168**)?

121

With no time for a 'softly, softly, catchee genie' approach, you immediately wish for djinn tears.

The djinn rolls his eyes as if it's the umpteenth time this has happened today and points to yet another sign on the wall: WISHES NOT RELATED TO MOULD PRODUCTION, CALL THIS NUMBER.

Picking up the nearest phone, you call the number.

Turn to **278**.

122

Groping blindly in the darkness, you stagger painfully to your right, fearing for your life.

Leaving the unearthly noise and confusion behind you, your straining eyes make out flickering lights ahead.

Each step sends a ripple of agony through your back as you hurry away from the scene of danger, slowed by your blood-soaked shoes.

You come to a stone corridor lit only by a solitary torch fixed to the wall.

By the light of the guttering flame, you make out two doors. Each has a thick iron bolt and a strange archaic rune inscribed into the woodwork.

To push through the door etched with the rune of a man, turn to 14.

To push through the door etched with the rune of a woman, turn to 221.

123

Ignoring the phone, you immerse yourself in the familiar dull warmth of data entry. After a while a gnome tuts and takes the call from its desk.

You enter the mysterious data with ease until you get to a client whose date of birth is listed as 'the second rising of the eighth frost moon of Rodaar, in the closing remnants of the third harvest'. This messes with your dd/mm/yyyy cell formatting no end.

A noise behind you like someone kicking over a set of wooden clocks distracts you from entering more data.

Turn to 267.

124

You tiptoe into the plush room, past the snoring security elf and his country-feast pillow. You read the strapline on the box:

King Wenceslas Pizzas
Deep pan, crisp and even

The strapline is indeed a witty one, but did it tickle you?

If it did, turn to **243**.

If you didn't register any mirth, go to **250**.

125

As the photocopier-repair gorgon advances down the tunnel, you search for the end of the tape, but it's like it's not even there! Your fingernails scrabble uselessly at a seemingly uninterrupted loop of tape, turning it round and round in your hands as if you expect it to magically appear! You have no alternative but to fight the lethal looker bearing down on you.

PHOTOCOPIER
REPAIR GORGON   APTITUDE **12**   ENDURANCE **8**

If at any time in the fight you throw a 7, turn to **145**.

If you defeat the gorgon, turn to **230**.

126

Your lack of academic achievement doesn't impress the imp, who tells you you're not really cut out to be a PA for top-brass management but he's willing to give you a go on a three-month-probation basis.

You settle down at the tiny PA's desk and immediately a magical chimp starts replacing your cake name on the office door with IMP (MBA).

You lighten your mood by customizing your screensaver and making a photo of a desert island your computer

desktop. The imp asks you to 'tie up diaries' for a big meeting next week and within minutes you haven't time to update your CV, never mind apply for another job. Besides, the imp relies on you and nothing would get done if you were to leave.

Unshakeable in your belief that you do all the work around here, your adventure ends.

127

The white-collar mermen are busy approving a product and fail to notice you bobbing above.

A tonsured merman floats next to a whiteboard holding a fat-tipped marker pen. The others are passing a prototype shiny pink holepunch between them.

'It's different,' says one, weighing up the holepunch.

'And sassy,' adds a colleague. The tonsured merman writes *different and sassy* on the whiteboard.

'I'm not yet convinced,' says another, stroking his chin. 'The man in me thinks a pink holepunch is an awful product . . . but the fish in me *loves* it and when I say *loves*, I mean LOOOOOOVES.'

Desperate for air, you pop another bubble and the mermen quickly turn round and snort as much briny water as they can. They are trying to smell your fear!

Count the number of fingers you currently have saving previous pages in the book.

If you have more than two fingers saving previous pages in the book, turn to **112**.

If you have fewer, turn to **171**.

128

The Portal cracks and smoulders into nothing as you dash headlong across the office to a white-hot fax machine steaming away in a corner.

It's a race against time to get your timesheet sent before the fax machine melts!

Your heart sinks as you realize one dread decision lies between you and salvation.

To send the fax face-down, turn to **169**.

To send it face-up, turn to **148**.

To send it face-down dialling nine for a line, turn to **244**.

To send it face-up dialling nine for a line, turn to **142**.

129

In a dangerous office, authority could provide valuable protection from undesirables.

With this in mind, you pull on the cloak of middle management, hiding in its velveteen folds.

You hope that the hood will hide your frightened human face, and the job title will hide your lack of experience.

In the pocket of the cloak you find the job description for 'Head of Assignment'.

Leaving the Wurst Witch's office through a door marked MANAGEMENT ONLY, you drift down a well-polished corridor, push open a single copper door into a private office and can scarcely believe your eyes.

Through the glass walls you see a collection of curious

beasts carrying out low-skilled admin work in a huge open-plan office. A row of elves are chattering into headsets while a centaur franks mail with great gusto.

A dwarf walks slowly towards a pool of typing gnomes, balancing many teas on his short arms.

Within moments a magical chimp is chiselling your cake name into the glass door. You feel like you've arrived.

Looking around, you see a tiny desk in the corner of your office, which clearly belongs to your PA. On the desk is a note saying she's out of action after getting her foot trapped in a bulldog clip.

You look out at all the downtrodden workers under your command and feel terrible – these creatures are lost in this world. A will-o'-the-wisp has been reduced to tears trying to fathom a complicated mail merge. A bumweasel looks on with melancholy compassion.

Desperate to free these creatures, you sit at your plush executive desk to come up with a plan of action, but are immediately distracted by a fat line of white powder gleaming irresistibly across your mousemat.

To snort the white powder up your nose, turn to **167**.

To leave the white powder and get down to some work, turn to **64**.

130

The last giant falls against the sink, creating a geyser-type situation.

Searching the deep pockets of your foes, you find that the giants have £83.02 in snack money between them.

You use the 'cash of the Titans' to empty a vending machine that also does ghee.

Gain 10 ENDURANCE points, or 11 if you like ghee.

Replete and bursting for the loo, you hop urgently to the toilet.

Turn to **191**.

131

A whirlwind of orc consumes the room and you opt to steal away.

As you leave, you notice a lift key-card by the door and you literally steal that away too. Finally, you help yourself to Orom's stout sword and a set of pens, as you don't know which is mightier round here.

Turn to **24**.

132

As you walk down the ill-lit corridor you feel no guilt at having blatantly cheated your way through the last fight. There are probably few people in the office you could take if it came to having a square go – but now you reckon you've just felled a headhunter? That's a whopper of a lie and no mistake. You probably haven't had a real fight since school. That said – who's to know? Feeling like a right rogue, you smirk east down the corridor.

Turn to **19**.

133

Keenly you root around in the sandwich man's basket

but there's nothing you fancy and he's run out of soup.

However, there's something magnetic about the basket. No matter how little you want anything from it, you cannot stop yourself from sifting again and again through its contents.

Finally you pull yourself away. No, hang on. Maybe the brie-and-cranberry baguette. Maybe not. Hmm. The bread looks a bit cakey.

Paralysed by the basket's curse magic, you spend the entire weekend locked in indecision over a western egg croissant and a withered duck wrap before dying a peaceful yet hungry death in a copse area.

Your adventure ends here.

134

If a tree falls over in an open-plan sales office, it makes a massive sound. As you hack a bough from their felled colleague, the treefolk point many twiggy fingers accusingly in your direction.

'Hoooom . . . you . . . have . . . slain . . . our . . . choreographer!'

Relatively quickly your blood runs cold, until you realize one of the trees is fanning you with an amateur-dramatics flyer.

It seems the sales team has been rehearsing a show as an after-work activity and you have smitten their dance teacher.

You could make good your escape: **91**.

Or make theatrical amends: **177**.

135

You explain to the centaur that he has been teleported into this world through illegal necromancy and the sacrifice of many temps, and that the Regional Accounts Director is the person to blame for this.

But the centaur is putting so much energy into pretending to listen, he isn't actually listening. Still, he seems to like you.

After a while you give up, deciding that postal logistics are not for you.

Turn to 7.

136

Despite the raging heat, you are too vain to take your clothes off in front of a row of sewing phoenixes.

With your face now doubly red from the shame and the murderous heat, you collapse weakly over a desk you could fry an egg on, and your cloak goes up in flames.

Within seconds, the fire has spread from your clothes to the ceiling. Soon the entire sweatshop is on fire. Even the trolls are sizzling deliciously like bacon.

As your body is consumed by the insatiable blaze, you vow in the next life to fit a smoke alarm in every room in your home and check the batteries regularly. That cannot be stressed enough.

Your adventure ends here.

137

You trek down an over-lit corridor, following signs

marked TOILET, passing a corrugated-iron kitchen door. A disgusting noise like hundreds of pigs troughing down on slops in a cavernous feeding hall echoes around it.

To keep following the signs for the toilet, turn to **191**.

To investigate the kitchen, turn to **272**.

138

Sneering condescendingly, you deign to inform the receptionist that you are a data-entry professional, contracted in for short-term consultancy work.

The receptionist's unblinking milky eyes hold you in their scornful gaze for what feels like an age of the Earth. Then she tells you that all temps must wait in the staffroom.

You enter the staffroom, which is a low, squalid box of a room, as gloomy as the reception. A great many wooden staves lean against the walls. There's barely space to stand upright and you're convinced that the receptionist has directed you to the wrong room when a thin man limps in on an orthopaedic shoe.

He introduces himself as Bernie Ditter and makes gun fingers at you. You introduce yourself and accidentally poke him in the eye with one of your gun fingers.

Bernie Ditter mumbles something about that being the last thing he needs with all the blackouts. Assuming this to be a medical condition of a private nature, you silently follow him out of the cupboard. As Bernie Ditter leads you into an open-plan office, you sense the presence of death upon him.

Turn to **22**.

139

Deciding the director's ID is not something you need right now, you continue up the steep incline while the voice on the Tannoy continues to remind you that a director's ID is something that you *do* in fact need.

By the time you get to the landing at the top of the room you are beginning to regret your decision not to turn back. Then you see something that puts all thoughts of fake ID out of your mind.

Normally the sight of a Hydra would *almost* stop your heart. But you were so stressed by your lack of ID that it literally *did* stop your heart. You die of a heart attack, literally.

140

You keep your eyes fixed firmly on the cake minxer, penetrating her with your icy glare.

She jerks forward nervously and the health bar topples from the desk to reveal what looks to be a sausage key.

Your eyes dart to some strange filing cabinets to the right with keyholes which would *definitely* fit a sausage.

A breeze gathers, bringing the windchime to life, and you hear the oily slap of wurst on wurst.

Perceiving your suspicions, the crone snarls at you,

revealing gums like *kiełbasa*! This is no saccharine soothsayer. This is the WURST WITCH!

'So you won't be tricked!' she cackles. 'Then have a treat!

'Choose a curse,' she demands, pointing to a wall of withered pork parchments. 'Anything on the top row. Between the weeping pustules and the beard of bees.'

You have seconds to decide on the nature of your curse.

To choose the Curse of Tape, turn to **175**.

To choose the Curse of Wits, turn to **265**.

141

As the axe finds the door again, sweat runs into your eyes, and you wipe it away with the sleeve of your top.

You glance at the Portal and the Regional Accounts Director's voice echoes in your head.

'. . . powered by the blood of temps.'

Quickly you cup your hand to your bleeding shoulder and fling the collected 'house red' at the Portal. The room is bathed in a heavenly white light blazing from the now-active Portal, illuminating the last remnants of the office door as it is trampled down by the frenzied mob.

What blood type are you? If you don't know, find out!

If you are blood type A, turn to **61**.

If you are blood type B, turn to **154**.

If you are blood type AB, turn to **30**.

If you are blood type O, turn to **198**.

You push your timesheet face-up through the flaming fax machine, dialling 9 for an outside line.

Resigned to your fate, you look stoically around the burning office. All the mythical creatures have now passed through the Portal, leaving you alone except for a fireball which may have once been an accountant. If it wasn't for the excessive heat and splintering wood-work, you would really enjoy the peace and quiet.

In a daze, you walk slowly out of the Regional Accounts Director's office, lumbering down the stairs and through the deserted lower admin offices.

What a day, you think as you amble through the blazing building, masonry and girders crashing around your head.

Smouldering like a barbecue, you arrive back in reception and sign yourself out. You look around for the receptionist to say goodbye but she's nowhere to be seen. Actually, reception itself is nowhere to be seen, as you are standing among the charred bricks of the building's entrance.

A firefighter pulls you out of the rubble and calls you a pranny for dawdling in a burning building. Giggling sheepishly, you realize it *was* a bit silly.

A week passes and you visit a cashpoint, yet no money has been paid into your account. You must have faxed your timesheet incorrectly!

With little money, you make your way back to your

regular J D Wetherspoon and begin to read from a mighty menu, its familiar purple prose soothing your sooty mind.

Bangers 'n' Mash: Three tasty bangers on a bed of Maris mash, all topped off with a leafy onion gravy. Alternatively why not try chips instead of having mash? And fish instead of sausage?

You treat yourself to the fish-and-chips version of the bangers and mash and chuckle knowingly to yourself. What a day!

The End . . . ?

143

Your attack goes badly and you turn to stone with one direct look from the gorgon's eyes. The gorgon looks irritated with this outcome.

'Are you just going to stand there? What is wrong with you people? Hello? Why does everyone ignore me? I know you all go down the pub at lunchtime. I don't know why I even bother.'

In a right old huff, the gorgon slides up the corridor, leaving you in a stony silence. Your adventure ends here.

144

Straining against the security magnet, you move as rapidly as you can towards the painted door. Your strength holds, but you grunt like a female tennis player struggling to adapt to the demands of the modern game.

Moving inexpertly, you collide with a wall of griffin. The griffin has no fillings whatsoever and the magnet does not affect him.

Desperately you try to push your way past and into the secret passage, but the griffin is keen to impress his new staff.

'Not on my watch, sunbeam,' he says, frowning with a single brow.

Then he produces a wireless keyboard and asks you if you 'know what's coming next, sunbeam'.

So near, yet so far. You are attacked to death by a griffin with a wireless keyboard.

Your adventure ends here.

145

Unwittingly you meet the dread gaze of the photocopier-repair gorgon. As you become petrified on the spot you decide your last pose will be one of openly flicking the V. Your adventure may have ended but at least your statue is not congruent with the décor.

146

In your mind, imagine a dad rowing a boat with his family in on a very choppy sea.

The mother and two sons have gone green and are holding their hands over their bulging mouths. Morale is decidedly low. The kids want to go home. They can't.

In your mind, look at each of them in turn. If any is sick (including the dad), turn to **159**.

If none of them retches, turn to **34**.

147

You declare the answer B.

The sphinx laughs childishly. 'Ha ha! No! The answer was C!'

Quick as a flash, you tell the sphinx that she interrupted you and you were about to declare the answer B . . . to be the *wrong* answer, because the right answer is clearly C, as everyone knows. It's a well-known riddle.

The sphinx is put out big-time and tells you to confirm what you really think the answer is, and if the wrong answer comes out of your mouth there will be t.r.o.u.b.l.e.

Turn to **255**.

148

Your timesheet judders through the slowly melting fax machine then itself starts to melt, which would be very odd if it wasn't made dull in comparison with everything else that has happened today.

Stuffing a desk blotter into your mouth to keep out the smoke, you run across the office and crash through a window. Your body tumbles wildly through the air towards the pavement, surrounded by a shower of broken glass, and you mercifully black out before you hit the concrete.

Many days later you awake groggy in a hospital bed with your legs in plaster. It is night-time and the ward is dark. Only the intermittent beep of your breathing regulator breaks the silence.

You wonder how many days have passed and whether your timesheet ever arrived.

Your blurred vision begins to make out a soft glow getting steadily brighter and approaching your bed.

An albino voice hisses, 'You forgot to sign out!' and the receptionist's vampire fangs sink into your neck, making your world a milky blur. Your adventure ends here.

149

Ambling half-heartedly along the dark corridor, you find a copy of the *Sun* newspaper with the sudoku puzzle already filled out. Sighing, you press on down the tunnel.

Turn to **80**.

150

Cautiously you glide past the dancing dwarf. His pupils have rolled back into his temples, leaving his eyes glassy and white.

As you step into the open lift, the dwarf senses you and begins bobbing towards you in a very needy way.

You press the button for the top floor but the doors do not close. The dwarf is up against you now, badly swinging his plaits. Hoping to placate him, you dance a little in return.

This only makes the dwarf needier and he dances up against you with the rhythm of the night.

This will be a sad yet easy fight, a necessary dance of death.

NEEDY DANCER   APTITUDE 2   ENDURANCE 1

If you put out the needy dancer's lights, turn to **227**.

151

You scan the sweatshop for a djinn or something containing djinn tears, but the shimmering heat and sweat in your eyes begin to blind your senses. Overwhelmed by the temperature of the phoenix combustion, your mind starts playing tricks and a nauseous, out-of-body faintness washes over you.

You are about to collapse!

Make and stir a hot drink. With the warm spoon, approach a friend or acquaintance and hold it on the back of their neck.

If they take it in good humour, turn to **86**.

If they become waspy or you don't dare do it, turn to **192**.

Disclaimer: Overheating a warm spoon may result in a hot spoon. Hot spoons may cause personal injury, blistering, breach of skin, nausea and scorching when pressed against necks. Enjoy warm spoons responsibly.

152

You charge after the light-fingered ranger, hurdling bushes and jumping over ditches. You spring high over a fallen tree-trunk and bound determinedly above a badger's sett.

Jumping is a great relaxant and you soon forget about your buzzard and even your quest to retrieve the One File. Jumping is the thing.

Without a care in the world, you join a herd of gazelles and continue jumping for many moons until a forest troll eats you as you graze one day. Your adventure ends here.

153

The imp asks if you have 'come far'. You tell him 'not really'. The imp asks you about your previous employment and you begin singing like a bird.

Befuddled by the Curse of Wits, you remain unaware that the imp has tricked you with a magic air glyph and you are now the interviewee for the very position you advertised for!

Roll a die to determine the number of A levels you have (and don't forget to add two for lies).

If you beat a six, turn to **118**.

If you throw lower than a six, even with your lies, turn to **126**.

154

Your unusual type-B blood sizzles in the Portal as the baying office mob charge towards you, gnashing their teeth.

There is a sound like someone cracking a belt, and a fantastical creature shoots from the Portal and stands proudly between you and the murderous throng.

The creature has the body of a Friesian cow and the head of a miner.

'Don't ask,' says the miner head, 'I don't understand neither.'

Then, turning its full-beam helmet light on the mob, it advances.

Because you summoned it, the creature will fight on your behalf. Should it be defeated, YOU will have to step in!

MINERTAUR   APTITUDE 4   ENDURANCE 12

vs

ENTIRE STAFF OF
LOWER ADMIN   APTITUDE 3   ENDURANCE 87

Should you and your pit cow manage to triumph, turn to **26**.

155

'Code red. All staff to the regional accounts office immediately. Could all staff pop immediately into my office—'

You spring at the fiscal reaper but collide with a remarkably clean glass wall you failed to notice before. The Regional Accounts Director has locked himself in a glass office cubicle!

'They'll be here in seconds,' barks the dread accountant, leaning back and cradling his head.

Before the entire staff of Firetop Mountain arrive to do the Regional Accounts Director's diabolical bidding, you must decide on a course of action.

To read from the file, turn to **164**.

To butt at the glass with your shoulder, turn to **20**.

To bat weakly up against the glass with your face, often retrying the same area of glass in a way that suggests you haven't properly grasped the concept of glass, turn to **249**.

156

The approaching djinn is already in a huff as he strides over in a pair of curly-toed brogues.

'This better not be a joke,' he says while pointing to a sign on the wall stating NO TONIC JOKES.

'I haven't got time for buzzards or babies. I haven't got time for that at all.'

The djinn is a right jobsworth and is clearly feeling the pressure. This may prove invaluable in driving him to tears. In a bid to push his emotional state, you ask him why he's so busy.

'I've got two thousand rubber moulds to ship before end of play today. Look at this. I'm making moulds. I've got a degree, you know.'

Puzzled, you ask why the djinn doesn't just wish for two thousand moulds, but the djinn merely points to another sign on the wall stating ALL WISH REQUESTS MUST BE GRANTED FOR OTHERS.

To emotionally manipulate the situation and wish for two thousand rubber moulds, turn to **273**.

To barge straight in and wish for the tears of a djinn, turn to **121**.

157

Wearing an expression of grim determination, you pass through the green wooden door and stand at the edge of a silent forest in full bloom.

The undergrowth is dense and foreboding. This presents you with a dilemma as you literally can't see the treefolk for the trees.

Unsure how to flush one out, you sit down on a mossy hummock and unpack your lunch of berries and nuts. Before you can pop a single cashew in your mouth, three mean-spirited squirrels working as a team overwhelm you.

Soon you are bereft of victuals.

'These woods are no safe place for the unwary,' says a voice in a coarse brogue behind you. 'You would do well to keep moving.'

Brushing damp moss from your backside, you get up from your hummock to see a tall ranger wearing cycling shorts. Despite being the same race as you, the ranger declines to shake your hand.

If you are unencumbered by a buzzard, turn to **38**.

If you have a buzzard cloaked about your person, turn to **214**.

158

You've had quite enough banter with the sphinx, so you testily push a giant paw out of the way and march towards the huge stone door.

From behind, her voice rings out:

What has a sense of bewilderment and no head?

You're not sure what she means. Without giving you time to answer, the sphinx bites your head off and you die by sphinx eating. Despite months of searching, your parents will never manage to reclaim your chewed carcass from the filing labyrinth of Firetop Mountain. Your adventure ends here.

159

Under nausea's duress, you stagger against a water cooler. Desperate not to make a scene, you help yourself to a cup with shaking hands.

Bwaaaaaalk! You just drank a glass of neat sea!

You begin theatrically retching, and the fire sprite tuts in the gaps. You are forced to throw a sea sickie and will not be able to attend the crisis meeting with the other directors.

Lose 5 ENDURANCE points and your simple meal of berries and nuts.

As the fire sprite leads you to the sick bay, you hear it mutter, 'Funny that this always happens on a Monday or a Friday, isn't it?'

Turn to **107**.

160

You choose the Curse of Promotion!

Instantly the room is filled with bright pink light. Laughter echoes around you as the now-giant witch towers above you – fully restored to health!

You have been shrunk to the size of a chipolata!

The Wurst Witch lifts you with her black-pudding fingers and carries you to the filing cabinet. Inside is a tiny doll's-house office. You are dropped inside!

Already in the doll's house are other prisoners – tiny temps of a lesser ability who are busily tucking into a diddy German buffet.

The filing-cabinet door slams shut, there is the sound of a pork key turning in a lock – *kank!* – and you and your team lie wreathed in meaty darkness.

Your adventure ends here.

161

You step through the blue door and out on to the deck of the *Golden Scart*, a fine seafaring galleon – the office ship of dreams.

You are deafened by the crashing of waves, and, should you have a top-knot on, the wind blows it straight off.

Looking around the gleaming poop deck you see a high elf with an eyepatch waiting patiently by a fax machine while sea dwarves eat lunch at their cannons to optimize their time.

Taking your cue, you feast on a simple meal of berries

and nuts, careful to avoid the swoop of gulls. Gain 5 ENDURANCE points.

You scan the deck for an accident book and notice a parrot wearing a triangular hat with the words OFFICE MANAGER on it. The parrot is squawking things like 'Flag it up' and 'You're one of the good ones' to passers-by.

On the other side of the deck is a salt-encrusted oak door, leading down into the ship's bowels.

Will you introduce yourself to the parrot (102)?

Or head below deck (85)?

162

You keep walking. As you press on, you come across a fiery pipefitter fitting a pipe to a wall. He displays the temper of a chef who gets angry with sub-standard work, but the skills of an ordinary pipefitter. He swears at you as you pass.

Turn to 9.

163

'You should have listened to my version,' cries the other orc. Suddenly and instantly a mêlée ensues between them.

Slinnk hits Orom. Orom hits Slinnk. Slinnk goes to fetch a weapon.

You pity the fighting orcs, as well as pitying the Minotaur you were forced to slay, all of them victims of inhuman trafficking.

Your pity turns to rage as you think of the temps who

fell before you, their blood leeched away to feed a diabolical portal of slavery. A fate that nearly befell YOU!

Guarding your tender back, you resolve to bring an end to this treacherous plan. The One File must be found and this Regional Accounts Director must pay.

The brawl between the orcs really is turning nasty.

You could step in (**216**).

Or steal away (**131**).

164

With shaking hands you open the file on to a P45 stapled with a Polaroid of a troll holding a BlackBerry.

'Chunkwar, Basalt, male,' you scream. 'PAYE ref. 2346504.'

A burning white light shines from the Portal.

'Freeeeeee!' screams a cracked voice, and the IT troll crashes through the office door head-first, flies across the room and disappears into the Portal, saucer eyes swimming with joy.

You try to read another P45 but from behind someone hurls a short sword into your shoulder and you drop the One File. Spinning around, you see the entire staff of lower admin advancing into the Regional Accounts Director's office.

As your vision blurs, you see two familiar-looking care-taker orcs battling their colleagues, screaming that you are their only saviour.

Sadly their cries go unheard. Like disciples in a crowd of baying heretics, they cannot quell the kill-frenzy of their co-workers bent under the will of their fiscal master.

Your adventure ends here.

165

Readily you agree to choreograph a treefolk musical and are given directions for where to meet later that evening.

On the hoot of midnight you arrive in the built-up rural area to be greeted by many trees in berets and root-warmers.

Possibly predictably, the musical is called *Ent* and is based loosely on *La Bohème*, telling the story of an impoverished telesales team struggling to survive in the forest.

You spend the next several months directing a musical sales thicket, which is not exactly how you thought your career would pan out, but it agrees with your work–life balance.

The first show is a sell-out but you are ancient by the time it plays. You manage only to live through the opening number, 'Sales Calls of Love', before becoming startled to death by an errant trombone.

Your adventure (after a huge opening number) ends here.

166

The elf moves towards you.

Fortunately the cheese from the pizza has sealed his eyelids shut.

Unfortunately elves have acute hearing and rarely need their eyes.

Fortunately this elf's ears are a bit blunt so it doesn't hear you that well.

Unfortunately the elf's sense of smell is ten on ten.

Fortunately his first arrow misses you.

Unfortunately the second arrow is a direct lethal hit.

Fortunately the second arrow hits a merman, who enters towelling his hair after returning from the adjoining pool.

Fortunately you take the ID card.

Unfortunately there isn't time to check out the pool.

Turn to **194**.

167

Bending over your desk, you snort up the white powder and immediately feel a tingling sensation run through your body. Without warning, your hairstyle shapes itself into a curly perm and your clothes transform into the height of 1980s fashion!

With a jolt of comprehension, you realize that you have snorted yuppie floo powder which has teleported your style back to 1985!

Lose 2 APTITUDE points for now being encumbered with a bulky Filofax and an oversized carphone.

Turn to **64**.

168

Desperate to stay incognito, you sit on your hands and ignore the attention.

After a while you wish the shapeshifter would sit on its hands too, rather than using all eight of them to goose you when your guard is down.

For the next few minutes the shapeshifter uses an arsenal of 'characters' to psychologically break you, with 'Little Chicken' and 'Aunty Dick Face' being by far the most memorable.

Lose 1 APTITUDE point.

After a while the bothersome creature turns into a frogspawn of breasts and trumps off to find another victim. Not wishing to be around when it returns, you slink out of the office.

Turn to **137**.

169

Your timesheet churns through the fax machine then

bursts into flames as temperatures reach the ignition point for paper.

Thick smoke now masks all the exits and your only option is to crash through a window and pray to the gods that you survive the inevitable plummet to ground level.

Shielding your eyes, you launch yourself through the window and plunge about three feet before colliding painfully with a firefighter climbing up a ladder to rescue you. Never more relieved to see a burly man with a moustache and yellow trousers, you are carried tenderly in his arms to the ground. Wrapped in a silver foil blanket, you watch as the Firetop Mountain office burns to the ground. Your ordeal is finally over and you have rid the world of the Regional Accounts Director!

The following week you check your bank account to find it . . . empty. Your timesheet never arrived!

With your heroism unsung you attempt to return to civilian life, hiding your battle scars under next season's clothes.

But a world of queues and terrible service is no longer a world you can stomach. No longer can you stifle sighs of disappointment now that you've tasted death.

An annoying ringtone in a crowded train carriage is all it takes to make you flash your sword. After that there is no going back.

Louts and litterbugs, vandals and vermin, women who don't have their purses ready at supermarket check-outs, all of them become your quarry.

With the smell of blood in your nostrils, you vow to slay the terminally rude and set out to 'clean up the streets'.

The End.

170

Breathing deeply in the womb-like safety of the stationery cupboard, you become less anxious at having seen a troll throw a cauldron of blood at a door on wheels.

Feeling a lot calmer, you re-enter the corridor, now ready for anything.

Turn to 264.

171

Feeling their steely eyes on you, you hold your watery ground and the mermen smell no fear.

'Your courage marks you out as an office maverick,' says the nearest, advancing on you with the holepunch. 'Tell us, human . . . what think you of THIS?'

Turning the pink holepunch over in your hands, you begin to feed back to them your constructive criticism but can only manage 'Bwaaaalk.'

Now desperately short of oxygen, you head for the surface as the tonsured merman writes *Bwaaalk* on the whiteboard.

Turn to 75.

172

Suddenly one of the serpent's heads notices you.

'Is this person being dealt with?' says the white head to

a green head, popping its glasses on and examining your director's badge.

'Nothing to do with me,' replies the green head blankly.

'Sorry about this,' says a gold head to you. 'Our head of department's away at the minute,' she simpers, gesturing to the stump of a severed neck next to her. 'We're a bit at sixes and sevens.'

'Sixes and sevens. I wish,' barks an azure head. 'I'm doing the work of a full hydra as it is.'

As no part of the hydra wants to take responsibility, it occurs to you that you could just attack it.

Would you be foolish enough to attempt such a thing (**99**)?

Or will you play ball instead (**202**)?

173

You return to your desk to catch a sprite dumping a heap of photocopying on it.

You don't want to get bogged down in chores, so you try explaining that copying isn't your job – but the sprite starts crying, then quickly turns angry and complains loudly about your lack of team spirit. You're not in the mood to be harangued by a waspy will-o'-the-wisp, so you ask where the photocopier is.

'It's next to the door of the Labyrinth Department. Cheers. I'll remember this. You're one of the good ones.'

The mysterious Labyrinth Department. The location of the One File!

Secretly pleased, you take the paperwork and strike out for the photocopier. As you leave, you hear someone mutter, 'That one's hard work,' but you press on regardless.

Turn to **88**.

174

You return to discover the hydra has been fired for gross misconduct and has been replaced by an approachable cockatrice.

You place an ent bough down before it and the cockatrice pecks it wilfully before nudging the One File over to you.

You clasp the file in your hands. The metal is so cold it almost burns.

At last you will be able to face the Regional Accounts Director.

At last you will have revenge.

Turn to **27**.

175

Note that you've got the Curse of Tape.

The Wurst Witch gives herself a hernia laughing before fizzling into thin air like a tooth dissolving in cola . . . but quicker.

Turn to **114**.

176

You search your brain for something witty to write in

the card, but the curse works its magic – your mind is a complete blank! Even the cliché card greetings are not available to you.

The skeletons shuffle restlessly, their bones making a noise like someone tapping spoons on a tortoise. With a trembling hand you attempt to move the pen on the card in the hope something will come to mind. But your hand jolts and you end up scarring across the card in biro.

'INFIDEL!' bark the skeleton army in unison. 'You have insulted our line manager with your meaty scrawl!'

You bluster that you didn't even know their manager, but now isn't the time to split hairs with skeletons. Drawing their scimitars they advance angrily – on YOU!

SKELETON STAFF   APTITUDE 9   ENDURANCE 12

> If you defeat them, nobody bats an eyelid and you turn to **120**.

177

Loudly you inform the advancing treefolk that 'the show must go on' and rack your brains for other theatrical superstitions to play for time.

A mossy tree informs you that the piece they are rehearsing is a rock musical or 'operetta'. He also informs you that they have been rehearsing at midnight in massively built-up areas to keep the show a secret.

While warming up and stretching it out, the mossy tree tells you he will let you in on their secret show if you agree to become their new choreographer.

To take up the role of choreographer of the treefolk's big show, turn to **165**.

To decline the offer, turn to **276**.

178

.ᴄᴄɢᴍ ꧁ᴍ ᴄɢɢᴘᴚᴍ ᴚᴛᴛ ᴛᴍᴧᴧ ᴛᴧᴧ
ᴧᴛᴛ꧁ᴄᴊᴄ ᴍᴛ ꧂ᴚo!!!!!!!!!!!!!!!!!!!!!!!!!!!!!!!!!

Your adventure ends here.

179

You choose to take the head of the gorgon, despite its awful droning song. Have you previously cloaked a buzzard?

If you do not have a buzzard secreted about your person, turn to **94**.

If you retain a buzzard within the folds of your cloak, turn to **231**.

180

The imp asks why you think you would make a good PA. You start telling him that your major weakness is too much attention to detail but then you realize that he's been complexifying your mind with a magic imp glyph.

Your fury knows no bounds and in your rage you assign the imp to toilet duty. The imp beams from ear to ear, pumps a fist into the air and says, 'Toilet! YES!'

He scurries out of the office just in time for you to answer your ringing phone. The familiar luminous voice of the receptionist tells you that the next candidate for the PA job is already on their way in. It's all go around here!

Turn to **229**.

181

Using your sword as a cane, you begin your ascent of the Escher-esque ledge. A soothing female voice pipes over a Tannoy:

'Welcome to the One File room. Please have your director's ID ready for inspection.'

You try to put this alarming news out of your head and continue your steady climb.

'The One File room . . . the room of the One File . . . where director's ID . . . is essential . . .'

After a while you come to a platinum door standing ajar with the words DIRECTORS' LOUNGE etched on it. A placard is bolted below it.

WARNING: *THIS ROOM IS SECURITY-PATROLLED 24 HOURS A DAY.*

Gazing into the corporate room, you see a security elf sleeping face-down in a giant 'King Wenceslas' pizza. On a plate is a director's ID badge. Literally on a plate.

Dare you steal in and steal it (**124**)?

Or do you press on without it instead (**139**)?

182

The elf is angrily dressing down the myopic troll for printing out a home-made novel about a subterranean romance which ends in divorce and a bitter childcare dispute.

The elf's fury mostly stems from the troll having written the large-print erotic romance on work time.

Before continuing, you decide to take a quick breather and have a nice sit down.

Turn to **59**.

183

A buzzard would clearly be a massive hindrance in an office environment. What would you feed it? Doesn't it need a licence?

Congratulating yourself on thinking this one through, you throw the buzzard in the nearest toilet with a satisfying *splosh-squawk!*.

Turn to **173**.

184

You press the button marked RECEPTION and a lock on the ancient door clicks open. You push your way into the dimly lit lobby of the Firetop Mountain office.

From out of the gloom a voice rasps, 'You need to sign in.' Peering through the murk, you make out an albino receptionist perched at a remarkably high desk and glowing slightly like some nocturnal mushroom. Her manner is rude but at least she's speaking to you.

The albino receptionist passes a leather-bound ledger down from the desk and motions you to sign in using an elaborate quill and inkpot. As you struggle with the giant feather, you notice that there are no other names in the book and every page is as hard as wood, having been thickly painted with Tipp-Ex.

If you feel it would benefit you to befriend the receptionist, turn to **45**.

If you perceive the receptionist to be beneath you, turn to **138**.

185

The hoots of derision continue unabated as you hop around with one damp foot stuck in the leg of your trousers, but you rise above the cheap shots.

This is clearly the best thing a row of phoenixes in a factory have ever seen and they roar with hilarity as you towel-dry your hair. You ignore them. Some of them have to wipe away tears of laughter as you brush your teeth and moisturize.

A dumpy phoenix falls clumsily to the floor in fits of mirth as it watches you tie up a shoelace.

You mutter under your breath that it's really not *that* funny and instantly the whole row says, 'Oooooooooh!' sarcastically in unison.

Turn to **32**.

186

The hike to Archived Purchase Ledgers is long and wearying but you are convinced it could be the location of the One File.

As you stop to catch your breath you make out a figure in the shadows. It is a tall man in a double-breasted suit, leaning nonchalantly on a pile of moss-addled files. The man applauds you like he means it and tosses a cigar in your direction.

As he approaches, you breathe in sharply. The man has made some of the worst piercing decisions you have ever seen. Both ears and eyelids boast row after row of hoops and studs, whilst between them his nostrils house a shiny golden bone.

'A pleasure to spend some face time with such an asset,' says the man.

The man massages your shoulders as he tells you that you're a great worker and that he could place you in a number of well-paid jobs. This was just what you needed to hear. His flattery and promises are working a treat on your self-esteem. You're certainly a cut above the—

Whoosh!

You duck just in time as the man slashes a scythe at your neck! From a squatting position, you notice the collection of shrunken heads around his belt and tremble with fear.

If you have a gorgon's head, turn to **242**.

If you do not have a gorgon's head, turn to **189**.

187

You pledge a wealth of money to the tree, hoping to receive one of its limbs in a quid pro quo arrangement. Unfortunately, the tree merely rustles in a voice like a bookcase, 'Hooooom! You . . . have . . . earned . . . the . . . trust . . . of . . . the . . . treefolk!'

You ask if the trust of the treefolk comes with a free bough and the whole office shuffles uncomfortably, like a tremor in a sawmill.

A short tree, which looks a lot like a coffee table you once owned, tells you they will gladly donate one of their boughs if you agree to vanquish their much-hated line manager. He goes on to tell of an evil faun manager who threatens them with cutbacks if they do not hit sales targets. Many of the treefolk look in terror at the beautifully sanded parquet floor.

You agree to help the treefolk. Turn to **68**.

188

Examining the framed poster, you read the word TEAM in gold lettering above the hive. A single bloodshot eye gazes down at you through a flap in the top part of the letter A.

A chill runs down your spine at the thought of being spied on. Suddenly you hear a terrible buzzing sound and your heart freezes with fear!

Terrified that the bees in the picture are coming to life, you windmill your arms stupidly around your head and run in erratic circles.

Eventually you realize the buzzing is an event reminder on your mobile phone. 'Begin work at Firetop Mountain plc,' it reads. A muffled snigger comes from behind the picture and the bloodshot eye leers patronizingly at you.

You quickly move away from the picture, silently cursing whoever it was who told you there is no I in 'team'.

Turn to **95**.

189

Without a gorgon's head you are unable to enter into the

headhunter's game of severed-head comparisons. With a fierce frown of concentration he extends an open palm at your head and you feel the crushing powers of his tribal magic. In some ways it's quite relaxing, like a massage, but in many ways it's quite painful, like having your head crushed.

If the Wurst Witch bestowed the Curse of Long Neck on you, turn to **56**.

If the Wurst Witch did not give you the Curse of Long Neck, turn to **60**.

190

On you push through the tangled undergrowth, deeply worried to have missed the second most important meal of the day.

Within moments you arrive at a clearing with the words SALES OFFICE written clearly in bracken on a big fern.

In you go: **5**.

191

You press on down the office corridor until you arrive at a door marked TOILET, then press the door marked TOILET and go into the TOILET.

The first-floor toilet smells wonderfully like pine trees and you are immediately confronted with an abundance of ablution options.

There are urinals no higher than your knees; there are cubicle doors that would fit on barns. There is even a hole in the wall with a crudely drawn biro arrow pointing to it.

The toilet is a private place. You must do what's right for you here. The following space is for you to enjoy your time in the toilet on your terms.

Now please wash your hands. Turn to 57.

192

Much as you like warm weather, it's too hot for you this. It's muggy. Ugh. Close.

You tell a phoenix you think you'd like to be sick, but she's too busy sewing and talking about Ruth's menopause to pay you any attention. You spy a large water butt full to the brim, but you would definitely need to disrobe before getting in.

> If you are too shy or would rather hit the gym and shed a few pounds before getting your kit off in public, turn to 136.

> If you feel comfortable undressing in front of a row of factory phoenixes, turn to 209.

193

You come round at the hooves of a centaur in an open-plan office staffed by creatures of myth and legend.

'Fear not, cousin of the forest, for we centaurs are adept in the ways of the post room.'

At his insistence, you hold the post bag open for the centaur as he continues to frank mail. The letters fill the bag fast and you learn he has worked here five long years, leaving his wife and four foals in another world. He also tells you about a massive mailout that's in the pipeline from the Labyrinth Department since a special file was moved there.

You could come clean and tell the centaur about the temps'-blood portal and your mission (**135**).

Or you could make small-talk and keep holding the bag (**66**).

194

You pull the platinum door shut and it instantly wizard-locks, trapping the elf inside. With the director's ID you press bravely on up the slope until you come level with a landing.

Then see a sight that almost stops your heart.

Turn to **62**.

195

The bubble wrap is snatched from your hand and you are pinned to the bed of the lake office by a tonsured merman.

With a free hand, you grab the fat marker pen from his shirt pocket and bite down on it hard.

Red ink fills the water and the other mermen dart away in fear! Yet the tonsured merman holds you fast as the poisonous ink fills his lungs!

You have one last breath. Take it now and make it a deep one.

If you can hold it for forty-five seconds, you will outlive the merman chairman and swim free (**75**)!

If not, turn to **211**.

196

You shuffle down the tunnel and nearly tread on a line of enchanted mice all dressed in pinstripe wizard robes. The mice are sloppily carrying buckets of water as part of a task to select a new sorcerer's apprentice.

As you tiptoe past the hopeful rodents, a bearded wizard starts furiously dressing down a clueless project manager mouse standing in a puddle of soapy water. An enchanted broom capers around stupidly in the background.

'You're way out of your depth in this task. You haven't controlled that bloody broom and you lost the support of your team. You're fired!'

You're intrigued, but not enough to apply for the job yourself, so you keep walking.

Turn to **103**.

197

You declare the answer A.

'How on Earth could it be the three ages of man? Foolish mortal. Your blood is forfeit . . . Your flesh . . . IS MINE!'

The sphinx's furious shriek strikes terror into your temporary-staff heart.

Bravely you run for one of the doors but are pinned to the floor by the scruff of your top.

Flailing desperately, you free yourself from the garment and place your hands on the cold steel handle of your sword.

Then the sphinx strangles you with a mighty paw and your face goes all o'er t'show.

Your adventure ends here.

198

Your common-as-muck O blood fizzles in the Portal, causing the mob to briefly stay their swords.

With a *bang!* like a violin whacking on to a kitchen floor, a creature swoops heroically in from the east.

White-feathered comes your saviour during your time of need, circling above and squawking at top whack.

The buzzard returns as a keeper! The buzzard will fight for you!

Because you summoned it, the buzzard will fight against the deadly tide of lower admin. Should the buzzard be slain you must step into the breach YOURSELF!

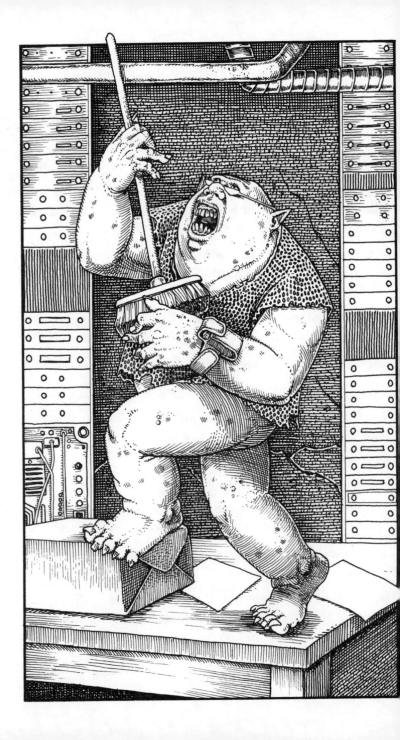

BUZZARD THE WHITE	APTITUDE 10	ENDURANCE 12
vs		
ENTIRE STAFF OF LOWER ADMIN	APTITUDE 3	ENDURANCE 21

If you and your hoary hero are in any way victorious this day, turn to **26**.

199

With no buzzard for company, you lie supine in your hammock, writhing in feverish agony.

Aside from a leprechaun bursting in every five minutes going, 'What's the *craic!*', no one visits you at all.

In a fitful sleep you dream a leviathan rises up from the ocean depths and rips off half of the ship. Then you get an advertising jingle stuck in your head and can't get it out. Round and round it goes.

This kind of thing could go on for days and you have no alternative but to fight the dread seasickness!

DREAD SEASICKNESS	APTITUDE 1	ENDURANCE 2

If you defeat the nautical nausea, turn to **41**.

200

From your vantage point you see a craggy-featured hulk dressed in a chainmail waistcoat. On his wrist is a mobile phone in a leather holster.

With a broom, he is banging steadily away at a blocked drain set into the ceiling. Liver spots glisten on his thick grey arms.

'Still getting the blackouts, I see,' natters the tea lady, pouring the oversized aberration a pint of tea.

'Another clot in the pipeline. Just waiting for the anti-coagulant to kick in.'

From above, the drain gurgles and unblocks, releasing what looks like day-old blood into a cauldron below. The brutish broom-handler deftly plugs an ethernet cable into the side of the cauldron using baguette-sized fingers.

Settling herself under a poster with the caption YOU DON'T HAVE TO BE A FEARSOME MEMBER OF A MYTHICAL RACE TO WORK HERE . . . BUT IT HELPS!, the tea lady rubs her legs and complains about her 'pins'.

Hang on.

Chainmail waistcoat? Thick grey arms? Fingers like baguettes? Motivational troll poster?

This isn't a run-of-the-mill IT technician. This is a daylight-fearing son of the soil. This . . . is a troll!

Test your luck!

> If the two dice you roll are higher than your OFFICE LUCK score, turn to **31**.

> If you roll lower, turn to **240**.

You regain consciousness in some kind of metal box with the sick feeling that you are moving. From underneath comes the sound of squeaking wheels and, with a jolt, you realize you actually *are* moving!

Frantically you search for a way out of this prison, your body becoming alarmingly cold. With a lurch, you feel yourself descending . . .

Turn to **3**.

'Just one form I need you to fill out, then the One File's yours,' slithers the gold head as the green head passes you the form in its mouth.

'Then, as Firetop Mountain policy, we ask that all directors taking the One File must first action a task in one of our sister companies.' The head flicks a forked tongue at three round doors.

'We'd ask you to retrieve one of the following . . .'

Disappointed at your lack of proactivity, it adds, 'It might help if you write this down.'

'So we need you to bring back one of the following. Either the accident book from the *Golden Scart*—'

'That's a ship,' adds the azure head, rapping her vast cranium on a blue wooden door.

'The tears of a sweatshop djinn—'

'That's a genie,' says the yellow head, ghosting towards the middle red door menacingly.

The gold head slithers towards the final green door. 'Or

we need you to get a bough from one of the treefolk.'

'That's a walking talking tree,' wheedles the azure head.

Which prize will you hunt for, brave director?

The accident book from an office at sea (**161**)?

Genie's tears from a fiery sweatshop (**87**)?

Or the bough of a tree that works in telemarketing (**157**)?

203

Politely, you ask the chief auditor what it is they like so much about the pink holepunch and suddenly the place swims with light, revealing a seated feral drummer.

The drummer knocks out a catchy beat on a drumkit and a feral saxophonist takes his cue.

Before you can do anything, the chief has hold of a wireless mike and begins singing . . . at YOU!

> *Think of all the office stationery you've seen or heard*
> *Like staple-guns, dividers, pads and Quink™.*
> *There's a lot of office stationery in all the world,*
> *But have you ever seen a holepunch that is pink?*
> *Think!*
> *A holepunch that is positively pink.*
>
> *Well here he is, the Pink Holepunch,*
> *The 'two hole' Pink Holepunch.*
> *He comes complete with a two-year and pink guarantee.*
> *You'll see that he's a groovy cutter*
> *With all metal working parts and a confetti shutter.*
>
> *He's the Pink, Pink Holepunch,*
> *The rinky-dink holepunch,*
> *And it's as plain as your hat*

*That he's the one and only truly original
Holepunch pink from lid to cap!*

*Yes he's the one and only truly original
Holepunch pink from lid to cap!*

Sensing that the cult-crazed canines are going to hit it again from the top, you slink away to **19**.

204

You skilfully throw a piece of scrap paper into a bin. Gain 1 APTITUDE point and 10 Wrath of the Treefolk points.

'Hoooom! You . . . have . . . no . . . respect . . . for . . . the . . . skin . . . of . . . my . . . brothers!' a furious tree eventually roars. 'Rise . . . up! Rise . . . up!' he sluggishly shouts to his barky brethren.

Frozen with fear for quite a long time, you are eventually trampled by an enraged sales-team thicket. Your adventure ends here.

205

You knock at the door and wait, listening as a lot of shuffling and banging takes place behind it.

'*Cmuth taaath?*' says a voice politely and you go in. In the middle of an immaculately tidy room are two orcs, one short and one tall. The tall one sits at a tidy desk, calmly smoking a pipe. The short one is managing to look busy at a computer.

Aside from a circular table oddly placed at the entrance of the room, you notice nothing afoot.

'*Meth icj naawt klaar?*' says the tall one with a beaky grin.

You shake your head, abashed by your lack of Orcish.

'If you cannot talk in our tongue, then we will fight in yours!' screams the short one, producing a stout sword and advancing readily at you!

Turn to **49**.

206

At the end of the tunnel you are faced with the choice of two shiny doors.

The doors are so nice it's impossible to choose which to go through. However, they're absolutely identical, so you sense whichever you choose there'll be little regret and certainly no danger.

To choose the door on the left, turn to **261**.

To choose the door on the right, turn to **225**.

207

You stand up to peer into the neighbouring workstation only to see a man peering balefully back at you. This can only mean one thing: you are working next to a man with a horrifyingly long neck.

Your long-necked co-worker introduces himself as Jessie and cheerily informs you he is in the doghouse with the Archive Department for always putting the wrong filing references on all his work.

You realize too late that Jessie is as dull as boiled rice but chatty as a chaffinch.

Roll a die to test your level of small-talk!

If you roll 4 or higher, turn to **93**.

If you roll 3 or lower, turn to **239**.

Cautiously you approach the skeletons, fearing them to be part of some elaborate trap. Up close they are much less forbidding and, of the two, the left one is clearly the looker.

The humming is coming from a speakerphone set on dial tone and lodged in the ribcage of the skeleton pointing at itself. Without warning a spine-chilling voice comes on the line!

> *Brothers and sisters have I many,*
> *But that man's father is my son Lenny.*
> *For back in history I did stray*
> *And had, with Mam, my end away,*
> *So my own father I must be.*
> *But what is the name of my son me?*

The skeleton's riddle is a chin-scratcher and no mistake.

To answer the riddle with 'Me', turn to **217**.

To answer the riddle with 'Lenny', turn to **245**.

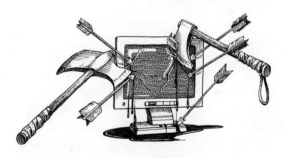

209

Bravely you strip off your clothes and plunge feet-first into the ice-cold water butt. *Sssssssss!*

What a feeling! Gain 2 ENDURANCE points and 1 OFFICE LUCK point.

Emergency over, you shake yourself dry on the factory floor and dress awkwardly in front of a row of phoenixes all making saucy comments, mostly derived from the word 'butt'.

The embarrassment is too much to bear. Lose 1 APTITUDE point for being a laughing stock.

To respond to humour with violence, turn to **269**.

To ignore the flaming factory fowl, turn to **185**.

210

You step into the gloom of the Labyrinth Department.

From what you can perceive, the labyrinth seems to be merely a single long corridor. The walls are lined with shelves which reach up into a murk your gaze cannot penetrate. Each shelf is weighed down with yard after yard of faded lever-arch files. Lichen grows unchallenged up their spines.

On the floor is an engraved brass plaque similar to those on park benches. The plaque reads: IN MEMORY OF PAM WILSON. SHE LOVED THIS PLACE.

At random, you pull a file from the shelves and blow the dust from its cover. The paperwork inside makes no sense at all. It is just reams of gibberish. You pull another file. They are all the same. Shelf after shelf of filed nonsense. But why?

Scoffing to yourself, you notice a sloping ramp falling away from you at a right-angle.

To press on down the filing corridor, turn to **277**.

To descend the slope, turn to **65**.

211

You are perilously low on oxygen and about to pass out when you suddenly experience a distinct rise in temperature and feel chlorine sting your eyes. When you open them you are surrounded by laughing children and mums in Speedo swim caps, and you paddle towards a lifeguard's kindly extended hoop.

Once out of the baths and changed, you stand in the foyer enjoying a pack of Monster Munch till your parent or guardian arrives to collect you.

As the familiar buildings slip past you on the way home, you begin to feel tired, so very tired after your junior swim.

Before you nod out, your last thought is that years of rest and play lie between you and the rat race.

Then your eyes finally close as, happily and peaceably, you drown in your own childhood.

212

Smirking unnecessarily you collect the djinn tears in a spare rubber mould, carrying it with the care of someone taking a watery ice tray to their home freezer.

You have very little room in your cloak to carry two things and decide, given the warm reception it got, it may be best to leave the buzzard here.

Although it tugs at your heartstrings, you give your

buzzard into the care of the clucky phoenix, who immediately smothers it in a maternal hug.

The sight melts your heart, but the sight of both of them bursting into flames hardens it again. Then the smell of roast chicken softens your heart a little bit, so in total you're feeling softer than when you started. You look expectantly at the smoking remains, but only one bird scrambles from the ashes reeking like a bonfire.

'Eeee! I had a lovely kip. I dreamt I had a babby!'

You leave back through the red door.

Turn to **108.**

213

Throwing your money around isn't going to help anyone, and you angrily push the sponsor form away.

'Hoooom! You . . . have . . . earned . . . the . . . mistrust . . . of . . . the . . . treefolk!' breathes the stork-infested tree, and the rest of the office eyes you suspiciously. It's like being given the cold shoulder by a furniture department and you could cut the atmosphere with a plunge-cut circular saw.

Breaking the wooden silence, a jolly faun line manager walks in and tells everyone to get back to work or they'll be for the chop.

Turn to **236.**

214

Sensing something is afoot, the buzzard peers out of your cloak and gawks at the ranger.

Both buzzard and ranger then communicate in a series of clicks and burrs before the ranger turns to you.

'You have a fine buzzard, my liege, but displaying birds is a pastime to attract unwanted attention.'

Before you know it the ranger has grabbed your hand a bit too tightly and is leading you pell-mell through the forest.

Turn to **253**.

215

With straining ears you soon locate the source of the humming.

The source of the humming is the two skeletons on the settee.

Turn to **208**.

216

As you try to separate the orcs you notice they are arguing about whose back-story was better as they fight. Orom is accusing Slinnk of using bad exposition while Slinnk is yelling that Orom has no substance to his presentation whatsoever.

You try to separate the orcs but the mêlée expands to include you. You struggle as best you can but your depleted strength is no match for two orcs with creative differences.

The orcs eventually simmer down and decide you are not the right person to champion their cause. You are then pinned to the door with an industrial stapler and left to die.

But death does not claim you! Three days later Slinnk is struggling with his daily crossword.

'"Blood may be thicker than it but that's all under the bridge now." – Five letters beginning with W.'

'Water,' you manage to croak, which pleases the orc massively.

From then on you are well treated and kept in a dark cupboard like a gimp and only brought out to battle the trickiest of conundrums – even when you're sleeping.

217

Feeling confident of your deductive powers, you clearly state your answer, 'Me,' to the skeleton.

There is a soft whooshing sound as a spring mechanism releases an arrow, which hits you assertively in the back of the head. Gain 1 Arrow in the Head. If you have previously gained 1 Arrow in the Bottom, you have now collected the pair.

You collapse to the ground and with your dying breath croak, 'Rosebud!' Neither of the skeletons is a cinema buff and, in many ways, the allusion and your last breath are wasted.

Your adventure ends here.

218

Is your gorgon's head the size of a conker (**228**)?

Or is it regular size (**96**)?

219

You scrabble sightlessly to your left. Your cut pounds in time with your racing heartbeat. Peril dogs your every movement and then you kneel heavily on a pencil. It isn't fatal but it *really* hurts.

At full pelt your head cracks into something hard, which resonates with a gonging sound. A door slams shut behind you. You are trapped!

A combination of blood loss and claustrophobic fear overwhelms your senses and you black out in the blackout.

Turn to **201**.

220

The accountant reclines arrogantly in his chair and begins his tale.

'There was a time when I was just like you,' he begins. 'Just a lone rat in a marathon, trying to pay the rent. These hands have cleaned pigs and scrubbed floors. Once I even used to work in HMV in order to make ends meet.

'I knew a business degree could change all that. So I studied hard until I learned the game inside-out, but where did it get me? Data entry! I had a qualification but I was still answering to a head of financial ops who didn't yet need to shave!

'I became disillusioned, and soon fell in with the wrong crowd. We did bad things. One night we went too far. We did . . . a Ouija board!

'It didn't work and everyone went home.

'But the next day I was visited by an apparition. An administratively capable apparition from another realm that completed my data entry for me while I looked up occult things online.

'The speedy and accurate work of the apparition turned heads. I began to climb the corporate ladder and even earned my own Portakabin.

'Soon I was able to usurp my boss. She was furious. Ha! You thought it was a man, didn't you? HA! Wrong!

'Swift then was my ascent to charterdom, yet no one knew my secret. I took control of the company. By then I had a boggart doing my filing and a magic vole doing my hair, but it wasn't enough.

'I wanted to expand production but I couldn't afford the wages. What was I to do? Cease trading? Did the pharaohs of Egypt let payroll stand in the way of their ambitious pyramid schemes? NO!

'So I conceived a gateway. A portal of entrapment powered by the blood of temps (no one would miss them, after all). All that was needed was one file to lock the low-waged workers here in this world. Under my employment spells, they are bound to this world and bound to me!'

'BLAAAARGH!' you shout in involuntary rage.

'That's a lot of noise from a temp. Someone whom no one will miss,' the accountant growls.

You feel alone. Very alone.

Frozen in terror, you watch helplessly as the Regional Accounts Director presses a button on his leathery desk . . . and pages the entire building!

Turn to 155.

221

You enter the ladies' toilets. With a sigh of relief you begin wrapping swathes of toilet paper around your body to stem the flow of blood from your back, but to no avail. Your makeshift bandage is quickly sodden and falls with a slopping noise on to the tiled floor.

You pick up armfuls of bloody bandages and open the lid of the sanitary bin to throw them away, but cannot believe the sight that greets your eyes!

The lid actually hides the entrance to a tunnel dropping steeply down through the floor! Voices echo up the tunnel and you bend forward to try and catch what is being said.

As you lean into the tunnel, an unseen assailant hits you smartly across the head with an electric hand dryer and you tumble down the tunnel amid a torrent of tattered toilet tissue.

Turn to **268**.

222

In bullet-point form, you explain to the sphinx that she needs to work on putting the *clue* in the question, not the answer. She nods like a badly oiled dashboard mascot and asks if she could work on putting your head in her mouth. You don't really grasp her meaning and there's no time to clarify because the sphinx is about to give you an exit interview . . . to the death!

SPHINX   APTITUDE 4.2   ENDURANCE 6.33 recurring

If you defeat this creature with a big-cat body and a woman's head that asks a lot of questions, turn to **47**.

223

Convincing yourself that you've become deranged with solitude, you decide on a 'water cooler moment'.

Uh! Uh! Uh!

Dry-humping the cooler is a great sensation and you feel no remorse. It's over too soon but what a rush! Then a feeling of insatiable depravity grips you. Your knuckles begin to contort as you begin lusting over that photocopier you saw on the way in.

Within seconds you are upon it, thrashing about violently and making copies of the whole sordid episode.

You have become sexually dependent on office technology. Soon you will die of a seizure, while trying to bum a fax.

224

All shaken to goodness-knows-what by the scary painting, you close your eyes, take a few deep breaths and calm down.

Unfortunately, when you open your eyes again the scary-man painting is still there and you get all windy again, causing you to close your eyes, take a few more deep breaths and calm down for the second time.

Feeling much better, you open your eyes and see the scary painting for a third time.

This time you really lose it. On trembling legs, you descend the thickly carpeted stairs and wobble back into the lower admin office, sobbing to yourself. A kindly hag calls your mum to come and pick you up. It's all been a bit much for you, hasn't it?

Your adventure ends here.

225

The door masks a ladder heading upwards. You climb up the ladder, pushing a trapdoor open and going through that as well. You arrive at a T-junction with two corridors branching off it, yet you're so weary from the tunnel that this information doesn't sink in the first time, so you have to be told again.

Turn to 277.

226

You pull out your unprized pink holepunch and wave it under the nose of the nearest feral auditor. Immediately the whole team put their noses to the floor in reverence!

'You have returned our most sacred artefact!' yaps the pack leader. 'The legendary holepunch! The prophecy is fulfilled! Whosoever wieldeth this punch may file the tax returns that blight our infidel realm.'

The pack leader keeps on like this for some time, but you're not really a religious person so don't pay much attention. However, it could be to your advantage to show willing.

To enquire further about the feral auditors' religious beliefs, turn to 203.

To not care about their faith system, turn to 10.

227

The doors close on the needy dancer and the lift speaks in a soothing female voice: 'Welcome to the One File Room lift. Directors are reminded to have passes ready for inspection.'

You press the UP button but the lift doesn't move.

'You are in the One File room lift. Thank you for choosing the lift.'

Suddenly the doors open again and two pale wizards with visitor badges pinned to their robes step over the dead dwarf and into the lift with you.

The paler of the two presses his employee's card against the lift.

'Going up,' says the lift.

Turn to **119**.

228

Not wishing to be tricked by the riddles of a tetchy sphinx, you pull out the fun-size gorgon's head, which laments at the sphinx in a helium voice.

'And?' sneers the sphinx at the head, batting it out of your hand.

The tiny gorgon's head rolls into a puddle of sphinx drool, and then something remarkable happens.

From the drool of the sphinx springs a small, white, be-winged horse no bigger than a butterfly. The tiny stallion settles briefly on the sphinx's nose, causing her to go boss-eyed before it takes flight again.

As an upgraded sphinx lollops after a tiny Pegasus into the labyrinth, you realize your adventurer's luck has held. You will pass through the door – riddle-free!

Turn to **47**.

Without even giving you time to make a cup of tea, two hobgoblins burst into the office manhandling a giant eagle. The giant eagle is clearly in no mood to discuss its CV, and pecks down one of its handlers before turning its rage on . . . YOU!

Swinging your mighty sword violently, blindly and inexpertly, you accidentally cleave the skull of the remaining hobgoblin, who was trying to help. By now the giant eagle is in a pecking frenzy, like a hungry chicken but *much* worse. You stand alone against this secretarial savage.

GIANT EAGLE   APTITUDE 3   ENDURANCE 14

If you destroy this PA of prey, turn to **97**.

You hit the gorgon a mighty blow and its head comes clean off, bounces a few times – turning the skirting board to limestone – and then rolls into a nearby hessian sack!

Before you can decide what to do, from inside the sack the head begins a long and soulful lament:

> *Alack I mourn my body fair.*
> *No more will scanner I repair.*
> *For all that remains is my icy stare.*
> *I've placed my head in a bag.*
>
> *No more will I in dead of night*
> *Caress the Cannon's catch-tray bright,*
> *Or xerox my rear by pale moonlight.*
> *I've placed my head in a bag.*

Let document go uncollated,
Paper jam unremonstrated.
For I have been decapitated.
I've placed my head in a bag.

Taking it with you could prove useful. However, it could also be a massive setback lugging a gorgon's head around the office in a hessian sack.

To take the head in a sack, turn to **179**.

To leave it where it is and venture into the Labyrinth Department, turn to **210**.

231

The buzzard sticks its neck out of your cloak and wolfs down an errant hair snake from the gorgon's head poking out of the sack. You wrestle with it under your arm, but the buzzard keeps going for hair snakes like an emu would go for a TV presenter. It looks like you can only carry the head or the buzzard, not both.

To heave-ho the head, turn to **33**.

To banish the buzzard, turn to **109**.

232

You stand breathless in the inky shadows of a thickly carpeted stairwell.

A door slams above you and, after a muffled conversation, the IT troll and the puffed-out tea lady re-emerge unencumbered and shuffle down the stairs and past you in the darkness.

Unseen, you steal up the carpeted stairs on to a torchlit

landing. In front of you is a giant portrait of a suited man, gazing down with burning white eyes and flaming red braces.

It is the Regional Accounts Director in portrait form! His very stance strikes fear into your heart, causing you to let off.

Lose 2 APTITUDE points.

To waste time by taking a moment to calm down, turn to **224**.

To gird your loins and knock on the door like you mean business, turn to **117**.

233

Moving fast, you lurch wildly down the basement corridor, now accustomed to the fact that your eyes will never be accustomed to the dark. You feel the steely cold of a door handle under your hand and you move inside just as the panel lights flick on overhead.

You arrive in a room no bigger than a stationery cupboard. Stationery is stored messily on shelves around the walls.

Breathing deeply, you feel surprisingly calm for someone who has just seen a troll, and are distracted only by a loud screaming noise which you yourself seem to be making.

You gaffer-tape an A3 Jiffy bag on to your wounded back. However, you have already shed a lot of blood. Lose 5 ENDURANCE points.

Take three deep breaths.

> If you feel calm enough to cope with the fact that trolls are real, turn to **170**.

> If you are still held in the vice-like grip of terror by the existence of trolls, turn to **256**.

234

On the intranet is a photo list of the company staff. You are surprised at how thin on the ground they are.

The workforce consists of:

> Bernie Ditter – Branch Supervisor
>
> Bronya Dodd – Receptionist
>
> Jessie Durham – Head of Archive Receipts
>
> D.W. – Regional Accounts Director

As you gaze at the photos, three things stir in your mind:

1) Jessie Durham has an unusually long neck.

2) There is no photograph of the Regional Accounts Director.

3) They used too much flash on the receptionist.

Shuddering at the thought of how many temps they

must go through to get anything done round here, you decide to knuckle down to some data entry.

Turn to **18**.

235

The centaur falls against the franking machine.

'You fight well, worthy adversary – perhaps it is you who should frank and I who should hold the bag?'

You decline the kind offer and apologize for the affront.

Deciding that postal logistics is not for you, you head out into the open-plan office.

Turn to **7**.

236

The faun line manager looks suspiciously like Bernie Ditter except with hairy trousers and 'hoofy' shoes. He sees you looking warily at his bloodshot eye and nervously distracts your attention by pulling out a wooden mobile phone and playing you his new pan-pipe ringtone. You tell Faun Ditter you think it's 'way cool' and he visibly relaxes, perhaps a bit too much.

Having gained his confidence, you ask in a low whisper how one might 'procure' a treefolk bough if one were 'in the market' for such a 'commodity'.

'You want a treefolk bough? I'll get you a treefolk bough. No problem. Let's do it. That one over there hasn't hit a sales target in weeks, so he's getting the axe anyway.'

Faun Ditter slyly nods his head towards a tense-looking tree smoking a cigarette and squeezing a stress owl.

Setting your sights on a scalable branch, you bring

your cutting-edge experience to bear . . . on the tree!

TENSE SMOKING TREE   APTITUDE 2   ENDURANCE 5

If you defeat the coniferous cold-caller, turn to **134**.

237

You put your own name into Google and find out you are either a jazz pianist or a wedding planner from Cincinnati with great testimonials. You jump as a voice from within a cubicle surrounded by shutters murmurs, 'Forgive me, for I have sinned.' In a a guilty panic you anxiously minimize the web window, realizing as you do so that you have brought up the company's intranet page by mistake.

To respond to your confessional co-worker, turn to **17**.

To investigate the intranet, turn to **234**.

238

Wishing for extra wishes causes another telephone to appear magically in your hand, and it is already ringing! Answering the phone, you nervously ask who is on the other end.

Turn to **278**.

239

Your small-talk is abysmal. Jessie is not interested in the Panama Canal. Neither is he interested in the Suez Canal. He has no interest in the Worcester & Birmingham Canal. Finally you mention that your chair is notably uncomfortable.

'WILL YOU SHUT UP ABOUT YOUR BLOODY BACK,'

Jessie yells, and angrily turns to focus on his work.

Feeling lonelier than ever and wishing you were on a longboat, you submerge yourself in data entry.

Turn to **18**.

240

The mind-blowing sight of a troll is too much for you. Still weak from your blood loss, you slump into a black stupor.

When you awake, you have been pulled from your hidy-hole and chained to the wall of a dungeon deep in the bowels of Firetop Mountain plc.

Every few weeks or so, a troll visits you to tell you to come out of the database so they can reboot.

Your adventure ends here.

241

If the Wurst Witch bestowed the Curse of Tape on you, turn to **125**.

If the Wurst Witch did not bestow the Curse of Tape on you, turn to **84**.

242

The headhunter begins a magic voodoo chant to try to downsize you. You take the head of the gorgon from its hessian sack and thrust it in his bejewelled face.

The headhunter lets out a short whistle to indicate he's impressed with the kind of head you're packing, then begins to calcify with a grating *crickity-crickity-crick* noise.

The last act of the headhunter is to hoodoo your gorgon head to the size of a conker. In a fit of annoyance you shove the statue of your adversary to the floor, stepping over bits of broken masonry as you leave.

Turn to **19**.

243

Involuntarily you laugh like a baying pig at the razor-sharp wit of the strapline. The elf springs to life, snatching up a tazer bow.

Testify your luck!

If your life has been unfortunately filled with very little good luck, turn to **166**.

If in life you have been fortunate enough to enjoy generally good luck, turn to **111**.

244

With your fax face-down, you dial 9 for a line then punch in the number of your temping agency in a staccato frenzy.

The fax whirs through as you fall to the floor, blowing on your scorched fingers.

You are crawling desperately towards the exit when another axe splits what's left of the door!

As you look up in disbelief, a burly figure with a pipe, garbed in yellow, grabs you.

It's a pipy firefighter!

Moments later you stand on the pavement, sipping sweet tea, next to the charred brick carcass of the Firetop Mountain office, destroyed for ever along with its secrets.

At the end of the next week you check your bank account and find untold riches lying in your account. Your timesheet went through! You recline in the lap of luxury and vow to do nothing with your life for the rest of your days.

But soon you become used to the lie-ins. Daytime TV begins to take its toll and the weekends quickly lose their meaning. You begin to feel restless, your sword arm itches.

It isn't long before you head back into the city . . . ready once again for the call of office adventure!

The End.

245

Tentatively you suggest 'Lenny' to be the answer. The speakerphone says, 'Thank you for riddling. Your answer is in a queue,' and with a click the line goes dead, leaving you standing in silence in a dark labyrinth with two comfortably seated skeletons.

It's then that you notice the better-looking skeleton has a small square yellow scroll attached to its chest via a very mild adhesive.

The scroll reads: 'When faxing dial 9 for an outside line.'

Puzzling over the true meaning of this clearly allegorical document, you unthinkingly wander deeper into the mystery of the labyrinth.

Turn to **81**.

246

You say your cake name aloud, which causes the woman to slam the gingerbread desk with laughter. A health bar topples from the witch's desk to reveal what looks to be a sausage key underneath it.

Your eyes dart to some strange filing cabinets with keyholes that would easily take a sausage.

Out of nowhere, a giant salami missile hits you full in the chest! Lose 1 OFFICE LUCK point.

The crone stands above you holding a jerky wand and sporting a frankfurter grin. This is no sweet-tooth sorceress. This is the WURST WITCH! You must face this hideous hag . . . ALONE!

THE WURST WITCH   APTITUDE 10   ENDURANCE 8

If you defeat her, turn to **89**.

247

- Regional Accounts Director uses portal run on human temps' blood to summon creatures from other worlds into this one.

- Creatures forced to work in dead-end office jobs for below minimum wage.

- Need the 'One File' to free them.

- Not rocket science.

Turn to **163**.

248

Feeling that ignoring the parrot was the *starboard* thing to do, you head directly for *right* in search of someone who might have an accident book.

On a long narrow board at the side of the ship is a group of humanoids, each tugging on a cigarette. They stand together like nicotine penguins, huddled against the cold.

It seems you've found the ship's smoking area.

If you smoke, you could light one up: **105**.

Or to search for the accident book below deck instead, go to **85**.

249

You are a fly.

250

Managing to find the King Wenceslas Pizza strapline in no way funny, you pick up the director's ID card and leave quietly.

Then you come level with a landing that you find in no way funny and see a sight that almost stops your heart!

Turn to **62**.

251

Glad to be rid of the recalcitrant ranger, you traipse through the copse, keeping one ear to the ground for anthropomorphic trees.

It's not long before you come across a short man in a plaid hassock carrying a large basket. He informs you he is the sandwich man, and asks you to let the forest know that the sandwich man is in the copse area.

The squirrel theft has left you with no lunch of your own.

Will you look in the sandwich man's basket (**133**)?

Or just jog on (**190**)?

252

You eat your lunch and try to strike up a conversation with the phoenixes, but they are all wittering on about the 'dilly wickins', which makes no sense to you at all. All of a sudden, someone asks you what *you* think about the dilly wickins.

You haven't a clue what they're blathering about and their expectant faces give nothing away. Hedging your bets, you assume it's something rude and make a bawdy joke about your own 'dilly wickins', leering suggestively at the beaky broilers.

It becomes immediately clear that you guessed wrongly as the whole row of birds gives you the cold shoulder. It's like the poultry aisle of a supermarket looking down its nose at you. Even a troll sneers in contempt.

Unable to befriend a single beast in the sweatshop, you curl up into a ball and eventually die in a hot, lonely foetal position. Your adventure ends here.

253

For many days you hike across rough terrain, camping on the unsheltered plains of rain-lashed marshes.

On the third day, the ranger stops and starts sniffing a forest clearing pensively.

'Orcs were here,' he affirms. 'There was a discussion about what to wear on Fridays, a fight ensued, then one of them shat up this tree.'

Before you can speak it's 'up sticks' and you're gone again, puffing o'er hill and dale.

On the eighth day you arrive weather-beaten and exhausted in an open-plan sales office staffed solely by treefolk. You turn to thank the ranger but realize he has made off with your buzzard (which to be fair was probably what both of them wanted anyway).

To pursue the stealing scout, turn to **152**.

To enter the sales office of the treefolk, turn to **5**.

254

Cautiously you step out of the lift into a bright, modern office corridor. Taking stock of the situation you see that, aside from the corridor going two ways, nothing fantastical is happening here at all.

To head down the corridor towards the icicles and snow, turn to **15**.

To head up the corridor towards the giant lollipops and candy-cane trees, turn to **6**.

255

'It is a really successful conga,' you declare strongly, causing the state-of-the-art lioness/woman-head to harrumph.

'So?' she sulks eventually. 'Here is *yet another riddle,* much, MUCH tougher than the last.'

You sense the sphinx has been sitting on these riddles for a long time and is eager to cram them all in. To ignore her musings would be futile, however.

> *My first is in AAAARGH! but*
> *never in MMMMMMMM!*
> *My second in RAAAAGH! and in*
> *RARAAARAAAAGH can be viewed.*
> *My third is in RAAAAAAAGH! and is*
> *just like my second.*
> *My fourth is in OOOOOOOOH! as in*
> *pain that is reckoned.*
> *My fifth is in WAAAAIIIEEEEE! as my*
> *point I deliver.*
> *I am used by apaches and come in a quiver.*

Solve the riddle by adding up all the letters in your answer using their corresponding positions in the alphabet! Now divide that number by itself and multiply the new number by 43.

Then turn to **43**.

256

Petrified beyond the limits of reason, your jaw clamps down on a thick wad of Post-Its until the fear subsides.

The experience leaves you drained but calmer. Lose 1 ENDURANCE point.

Now focused, you notice a motivational poster of a chameleon blending in with some foliage in an attempt to fend off prey. ADAPTABILITY, reads the poster.

Not for the first time in your life, you take the advice of

a chameleon, and realize you must be proactive. You manage to slow your breathing and only shout 'troll!' two more times.

Turn to **170**.

257

With one eye fixed on the Portal and another on a pixie who's going through your things, you watch as the IT troll and the tea lady approach a painted wall.

The troll punches a code into a keypad on the wall and it slides noiselessly open. The tea lady lugs the Portal through the wall with much grumbling.

You must follow the Portal but, as you try to move forward, the One File becomes heavy, like it has a will of its own. Then you notice everyone's weapons are pinned to the floor and deduce that the IT troll must have switched on a floor magnet. It's obvious, now you think about it.

Hold this book out to the side of you with your best arm. Do this right away and keep it held out for one minute.

If anyone notices and asks you what you're doing, turn to **144**.

If nobody notices or you just get the odd funny look, turn to **92**.

258

ᚠᚱᛗᚪ ᛞᚢᛒ ᛒᚾᛒ ᚳᛞᚱᛏᚷᛒᚳ ᛞᚢ ᛗᚳᛁᛒ
ᚳᛞᚳᛚᛗᛗᚱᚣ ᚷᛗᛒᛞᛏᚳ ᛈᛒᚢᚷᛈᚳ ᚷᛗ
ᛒᛒᛗᚱᚣᚳᛏᚪᚷᚳ ᛒᛒ ᚷᚳᚷᛒᚳᛁᛏᚳᚢ
ᚳᚷᛥᚪᛒ ᚱᛗᛒᚾᚷᚣ ᚳᚳᚵ ᚦᛒᛗᛗ ᚷᛏ ᚠᛒ
ᛒᛒᛗᚱᚣᚪ.

ᚣᛒᛗᚢ ᛗᚳ 178.

ᛒ ᛗᚳ 67.

259

Is a buzzard resident within your cloak?

Yes, a buzzard is in my cloak: **101**.

There is no buzzard present in my cloak at this time: **55**.

260

You grab the buzzard, encasing its feathery bulk in your coat.

Write down somewhere that you have cloaked a buzzard. The buzzard is now a keeper.

> *If you can talk with crowds and keep*
> *your virtue,*
> *Or walk with kings and not lose the*
> *common touch;*
> *If neither foes nor loving friends*
> *can hurt you;*

If all men count with you, but none
*   too much;*
If you can fill the unforgiving minute
With sixty seconds' worth of
*   distance run,*
Yours is a buzzard and everything
*   that's in it.*
And which is more – you'll own
*   a buzzard, my son.*

You've been fiddling around with a buzzard in the toilet for ages now, so you'd better get back to your desk before people start talking.

Turn to **173**.

261

Dead.

262

Hyperventilating, you stand triumphant over the prone body of the leathery-faced man. You stoop to take the trousers from your defeated foe to use as a tourniquet when you hear a sound like stone grinding against stone behind you.

Spinning around to see what latest threat you must confront, you catch a flash of one angry bloodshot eye before being struck violently with a wooden clipboard.

Darkness washes over you. Then foul-smelling water washes over you and you slip into a sinking sensation, smacking your forehead on a sink as you sink rapidly down.

Turn to **268**.

263

One by one the drow elves make their excuses and filter away from the cooler. You feel the true lonely ache of top-brass management, as well as irritation that none of the elves was actually drinking any water.

You try hanging around the water cooler by yourself and gossiping about that giant eagle, but it doesn't really work with just one person.

Then you find yourself pouring a cup of cool water. Cool, cool water.

You are about to slake your thirst when you suddenly wonder if it's a good idea.

Then two extra ideas fill your head. One of the extra ideas is sensible, whilst the other is off the chain.

To drink from the water cooler, turn to **35**.

To cut out the middleman and go straight to the toilet, turn to **191**.

To dry-hump the water cooler, turn to **223**.

264

Leaving the stationery cupboard, you come face-to-face with what appears to be a suited man with an over-realistic carnival bull's head. Steam billows out of its nostrils.

'Where is the staffroom?' the beast asks in a voice like hot gravel. 'I'm lost. It's like a maze in here.'

You manage to shrug before freezing completely with fear, your shoulders now in an unattractive hunched position.

The beast bears down on you, its red eyes burning in its very real head.

'What? You don't talk to interns? Too lowly for you, are we?'

Dare you talk to a Minotaur (36)?

Or will you ignore it instead (275)?

Did you fail to recognize that a man with a bull's head is a Minotaur? Don't be ashamed. Even the best adventurers struggle with beast differentiation. It happens all the time. At the back of this book is a bestiary which will tell you all you need to know about any of the creatures you encounter. Simply flip to the bestiary each time you're introduced to a beast you know little or nothing about. You'll never have to feel awkward again.

265

Note that you've got the Curse of Wits.

The Wurst Witch bursts into contagious laughter before dissipating in a cloud of smoke with a smell not dissimilar to bacon rind.

Turn to 114.

266

Careful to remove your shoes and any restrictive clothing, you leap forth into the icy lake.

Splooosh! An instant hell of cold. Then the realization that it's not so bad once you're in. The lake appears to have been angrily chiselled into the carpeted corridor.

Judging by the depth of the water, the floors of this building must be thick.

Diving down, you spot a jellyfish in front of you. It turns out to be a sheet of giant bubble wrap which you grasp gratefully. Biting down on one of the bubbles, you realize you can use it to breathe underwater.

Something shiny below you catches your eye and you paddle down towards it – mainly to see what it is.

At the bottom of the lake is a handful of chairs set out in a classic crescent conference style.

Filling the chairs are some of the most corporate-looking mermen you have ever seen.

Paddle to **127**.

267

Turning cautiously on your chair, you notice a small army of skeletons have assembled around your desk.

'Our line manager leaves us for promotion,' speaks the nearest in a voice like snooker balls knocking together. 'All must write in her card!'

The talking skeleton pushes a giant greetings card into your face.

Did you have the Curse of Wits bestowed on you by the Wurst Witch?

If so, turn to **176**.

If not, turn to **39**.

Down and down you tumble in a fever of disorientation till you hit a body of water with a *splooosh*. Gripped by a dervish current, you whirl deeper and deeper downward – unable to work out which way is up, so rapid is your descent.

Clunk! Splosh! Your head collides with porcelain and you break the surface of the water, panting heavily.

As your eyes become accustomed to the lack of water in them, you realize you are bobbing up and down in a giant toilet, the bleach stinging the cut in your back.

Revolted to the core, you clamber out of the bowl and lean heavily against a large Christmas tree which has clearly been serving as an oversized toilet brush. You try to make an emergency call on your mobile but it is sodden and unusable.

Still dripping wet, you slide under a hefty cubicle door, only to be met by a row of sinks no higher than your shins!

You are in an ancient bathroom which for some reason caters for people of drastically opposing sizes, yet with no disabled access whatsoever.

You are exploring the bathroom when a rhythmic booming noise from the next room stops you in your tracks.

With a racing heart, you peer through a window in the bathroom door to spy the tea lady parking her trolley in a room stacked with computer parts and monitors.

A sign on the wall reads: SERVER ROOM.

The thumping noise continues unabated.

Turn to 200.

269

Still wet and in no mood to put up with low wit from a bunch of under-skilled hens, you pull out your sword and ask if anyone wants some.

The phoenixes all cackle with delight at the innuendo, except the one you decapitate as an example to the others.

Quietly sniggering, the surviving seamstresses get back to their work, and this time really put their beaks into it.

Turn to 32.

270

You jog along a corridor down which echoes a distant sound of barking dogs, eventually passing over a tarnished brass plaque set into the floor that reads ARCHIVED SALES RECEIPTS. Could this be the hidden location of the One File?

The shelves in this part of the labyrinth have been destroyed; the floor is covered with shredded paper and ring-binder files ruined by teeth marks. Fixed to a wall is a photocopy picture of Jessie from the ground floor. The eyes have been scratched out.

On your hands and knees you sift through the ripped files in search of the Regional Accounts Director's One File. Your rustling of papers masks the approaching sound of heavy panting and many wagging tails. It is

not until you feel the quick, damp breath on your neck that you spin round!

Turn to **274**.

271

You choose the Curse of the Long Neck, which, you realize immediately, was a foolish choice.

Instantly you feel your neck grow another five inches. You look absurd, but hey, who's going to notice around here?

To keep adventuring with a stupid long neck, turn to **114**.

272

The incidents of the day have left you ravenous, possibly due to some magic, because sometimes magic causes a victim to be ravenous, so you decide to investigate the kitchen.

You cautiously push open the corrugated-iron door and enter a tiny room littered with crisp packets.

Squatting on a blue Ikea sofa are a monstrously fat ogre and an equally fat frost giant. The ogre has a two-litre bottle of diet cola to his lips and is squeezing it with chubby hands to speed up delivery. The frost giant is wrist-deep in a bag of frozen tripe.

The ogre looks down at you. 'Are you going to the machine? Get us Wotsits, Fanta and some ghee.'

The frost giant lets out a damp burp, the smell of which seems to send both monsters into a feeding frenzy.

With monster-sized appetites, they stagger towards

you. You're facing two giant dieters in the grip of a gorging mania and the main course is . . . YOU!

DIET OGRE   APTITUDE 8   ENDURANCE 12

DIET FROST GIANT APTITUDE 12   ENDURANCE 6

DETOX CYCLOPS   APTITUDE 6   ENDURANCE 10
(lying behind couch)

If you defeat these warlite weight watchers, turn to **130**.

273

You wish for two thousand rubber moulds and immediately a deluge of rubber rains heavily down on the phoenixes, perhaps a bit too heavily as it kills many of them. The djinn is ecstatic – it is a *lot* of rubber moulds!

In floods of tears he exclaims, 'No one! No one has ever been this kind. A thousand golden thanks!'

Yet before you can collect any tears a green djinn sulks in, jealously spying his colleague's bounty of moulds.

'Oh, I get it,' says the green djinn. 'Well, great. That's just great. You've done his moulds for him.'

You explain that you were only trying to help but the green djinn becomes even more caustic.

'Well, that's great. Juuuuuust great. It didn't occur to you there might have been a competition between mould makers or anything? With a ham as the prize?'

'Pipe down!' barks the first djinn.

'No, I will not pipe down, Gordon,' the green one retorts. 'I really wanted that ham.'

The other djinn's jealousy has got the better of him and he advances . . . on YOU!

JEALOUS DJINN   APTITUDE 13   ENDURANCE 3

If you slay this slave of the lamp, turn to **212**.

274

From a kneeling position you come face-to-snout with a pack of meek, balding men in grey suits, crouched on all fours with their tongues lolling out. The head of the pack licks your face suspiciously and wags a mangy tail which protrudes from the back of his non-iron trousers. One of the other dog-like businessmen begins to sniff at your bottom.

Looking around, the mystery becomes clear. You are faced with a pack of drooling auditors all turned feral trying to make sense of the Regional Accounts Director's sham filing labyrinth!

If the Wurst Witch did not bestow the Curse of the Long Neck on you, turn to **40**.

If the Wurst Witch bestowed the Curse of the Long Neck on you, turn to **8**.

275

You ignore the Minotaur altogether and head down the corridor.

'Please do not ignore me like the others,' it bleats. 'I am an honourable intern.'

You turn and tell him that 'honourable intern' is an oxymoron.

'WHO ARE YOU CALLING AN OXY MORON?' it screeches, then tugs hard on its nose ring to show it means business.

This is going to be a half-bullfight to the death!

MINOTAUR INTERN   APTITUDE 8   ENDURANCE 12

   If you defeat your cattle-headed co-worker, turn to **90**.

276

Desperate not to become caught up in a dramatic dingle, you make good your excuse and hurry out of the open-air office, stepping on a rake. Lose 1 ENDURANCE point as your eyes water.

Turn to **91**.

277

You arrive at a T-junction with two corridors branching off it. Fixed to the walls next to each corridor are two filthy wooden signs. One sign has the words ARCHIVED PURCHASE LEDGERS roughly scratched into it. The other sign bears the words ARCHIVED SALES RECEIPTS crudely daubed in dried blood.

To head towards Archived Purchase Ledgers, turn to **186**.

To set out for Archived Sales Receipts, turn to **270**.

278

CONGRATULATIONS! YOU HAVE CALLED THE MIGHTY DJINN'S WISHLINE! CALLS ARE CHARGED AT A PREMIUM RATE! PLEASE CHECK WITH THE BILL PAYER BEFORE CALLING!

PRESS 1 TO WISH FOR UNTOLD RICHES! Turn to **113**.

PRESS 2 TO WISH FOR MORE WISHES! Turn to **238**.

PRESS 3 TO WISH FOR TWO THOUSAND RUBBER MOULDS! Turn to **37**.

TO WISH FOR ANYTHING ELSE, STATE YOUR WISH AFTER THE BEEP! Turn to **51**.

279

You're bored witless by now and wish you had brought that copy of the *Sun* with you. Wishing won't bring it here though. You keep walking to **25**.

The Accident Log of the Golden Scart

Name	Species	Accident
Arbyr Valeshield	Gorgon	Petrified wrist
Valwald Odhausen	Cyclops	Confirmed blind
Mary Barleycorn	Hag	Swallowed paperclip
Lillistran Jofu	Unicorn	Trapped nerve
Fenrir Oxbane	Sprite	Retained spear in eye
Beezly Pippin	Gnome	Sat on
Bobo Foamwalker	Pirate monkey	Swallowed brine
Klanfurt Kelso	Majestic centaur	Face all chuffed out of whack
Tim Goodfellow	Gnome	Digested by Kraken
Ud Thh-n	Orc	" "
Thratt Lars	Sea trog	" "
Fip Gladraft	Halfling	" "
Behemo	Kraken	Digested by leviathan
'Flaming' Joe	Fire sprite	Missing, presumed extinguished
Elthiel Zazael	Imp	Knelt on pencil

An Office Bestiary

Ant   An insect belonging to the order Hymenoptera. Very much a team player. Individually ants lack focus and are an easily defeated opponent. Typing speed 14 wpm.

Armoured troll   See *Troll* and imagine it wearing armour.

Boggart   Malevolent spirit with distasteful bedtime habits such as putting a clammy hand on sleepers' faces. A well-managed boggart can produce work of a high standard but is prone to bad-mouth those in positions both of authority and of inferiority. Typing speed 28 wpm.˙

Bumweasel   A tubular mammal of low magical ability, the bumweasel's only talent is to be a talking version of a normal weasel. Argumentative by nature, bumweasels are best suited to lower administrative tasks. Typing speed 77 wpm.

Buzzard   Bird of prey which hunts over open land. Buzzards commonly breed in woodland and are best known as vending-machine prizes.

Centaur   Half-human, half-horse beast. Centaurs' pride and vanity make them easily manipulated workers for the cunning manager, and many fulfil roles well below their skill level. Typing speed 51 wpm.

An Office Bestiary

Cockatrice   A chicken with a lizard tail, the cockatrice is the product of a hen's egg hatched by a toad. Frequently the butt of office jokes. Typing speed 64 wpm.

Cyclops   Big fella. Only one eye. Not good on depth perception.

Djinn   A spirit of smokeless fire, this genie from Arabia is short-tempered and suffers from poor organizational skills. Its magical abilities allow it to quickly rise to middle management but it rarely progresses above this level into positions of seniority. Typing speed 66 wpm.

Donkey   Lowly beast of burden frequently used by djinns to carry untold riches. Hooves: 4.

Dosser   A human who has given up on office work to go on a 'gap decade'. A dosser will often use the giant 'sorry you're leaving' card it receives as a practical foldaway tent.

Dragon   A fire-breathing lizard of huge size and fearsome temperament. Many species exist throughout the world, the largest of which is the *Draco amplus concubitis absentis*, or big fuck-off dragon. Typing speed 1 wpm.

Drow elf   This dark-skinned, silver-haired elf predominantly lives underground. Folklore describes drow elves as 'mardy'. Typing speed 39 wpm.

Dryad Member of a creatively talented race of tree nymphs prone to emotional outbursts. Dryads copy a lot of people in on an email if they sense they are being blamed for anything. Typing speed 78 wpm.

Dwarf A short humanoid creature highly skilled in the field of engineering, now struggling to come to terms with a post-industrialized world. Their being hard workers but lacking in office skills makes dwarves first-rate 'go-nowhere' staff. Typing speed 10 wpm.

Elf Pale-skinned being with a gentle nature yet skilled in the deadly arts of warcraft. A magical ability to repel delegated work as if coated in Teflon is its key strength. Typing speed unknown.

Enchanted mice Hard-working rodents who will do anything to meet a deadline. Typical examples of this are pulling all-nighters, bewitching brooms and black-mailing Trading Standards.

Enchanted swan Large white water-fowl with the supernatural ability to use calculators and compile sales receipts. Its muscular neck can break a man's arm, legend tells. Talking speed 137 wpm.

Faun Merry little creatures, fauns are men with goats' legs and hooves. They use the bewitching melody of their pan pipes and S.M.A.R.T. management techniques to emotionally manipulate staff working under or above them.

An Office Bestiary

Feral auditor Independent assessor of a company's financial accounts. Prolonged exposure to a poorly structured filing system has driven the common auditor to revert from domestication to a feral state.

Fire sprite A sprite (see *Sprite*) composed entirely of flame and smoke. Its weaknesses include water, lack of oxygen, perfectionism and paper-based work. Personnel managers often struggle to find appropriate roles for fire sprites but recent changes in employment law requiring equal-opportunity measures ensure there is a disproportionate number of fire sprites in the workplace.

Flibbertigibbet Member of a whimsical race of delightful fairies composed of the decaying flesh of men executed on the gallows. The carrion nature of their bodies makes them ill-suited to catering work or office environments where buzzards are present. Excellent multi-taskers. Typing speed 72 wpm.

Fly Two-winged idiot of the air. Massively deluded office dreamers, flies have been known to 'act out' their fantasies for top management roles by bursting in on top-floor meetings and 'taking up the reins'. Flying speed 3 cm per second.

Forest troll See *Troll* and imagine a forest when reading the definition.

Frost giant Monster of human appearance but prodigious size and strength. Once great hunter-gatherers, frost giants now lack the time to prepare meals and rely heavily on the frozen-food industry. A diet frost giant will consume over a ton of defrostable goods in a single all-staff meeting which equates roughly to four family 'big shops' at your nearest supermarket. Plastic-bag-carrying speed 14 bpm.

Gazelle   Antelope of the genus *Gazella*. The best type is the Thomson's gazelle, which can reach speeds of 50 mph, has two long curved horns and jumps as a distraction method when fleeing predators. No description of the taste of its flesh was available at the time of going to print.

Ghost   Manifestations of the spirits of the dead, ghosts are frequently 'sighted' by co-workers 'haunting' the desks or PCs where they work. Children or adults wearing a white sheet over the head are commonly mistaken for ghosts but display none of the skill at manipulating spreadsheets that typifies this race. Typing speed WOOoooOOOOO!

Giant eagle   A bird of prey identical in all ways to the common eagle but built along the same lines as the largest of the dragon species (see *Dragon*). Good oral communication and diary skills make giant eagles best suited to PA roles (see *PA*). Typing speed 97 wpm.

Gnome   A diminutive bearded creature possessed of low magical ability, who generally makes his home beneath toadstools and tree roots. An approachable, inventive nature, often coupled with poor judgement, makes gnomes ideal candidates for marketing roles. Typing speed 72 wpm.

Goblin   Foul of face and fearsome of manner, this stinking creature bears some physical similarity to the dwarf. Its xenophobic attitude to all other races is currently overlooked but will cause problems when new race-related employment legislation comes into force. Will always over-promise and under-deliver.

Gorgon   Dread female monster cursed with snakes for hair by the goddess Athena. The gaze of the gorgon may turn any creature to stone, making this monster poorly suited to teamwork, team-building days, team-strategy meetings, team socializing, and any work involving the living. If found, the head of a gorgon may be redeemed at Argos for vouchers.

Griffin   Fierce creature with the body of a lion and the head and wings of an eagle. A griffin will typically suffer from the onset of diabetes in later life when its pancreas stops secreting insulin. Griffins are full of themselves and like to 'give it all that'. Typing speed 92 wpm.

Hag   Hags are ugly old women dressed in rags. The easy way to remember this is by using the rhyme 'hags in rags'. Fast workers. Typing speed 112 wpm.

Half elf   Member of a mongrel race of elves (see *Elf*) which have bred with other races. The non-elf part of their ancestry can be discerned by studying the individual's characteristics. For example, a half elf which does no work yet believes itself to be an indispensable employee will be the result of a union between an elf and a PA.

Halfling A hairy-footed creature identical to a human except in size, being approximately half the size of an average man, halflings are noted for their love of pipe-weed and snooker. No magical abilities but loyal to the company. Keeps strict nine-to-five hours and not a minute more. Highest break: 147.

Harpy Winged bird-woman with a furious face who uses her sharp talons to tear food from the hands of blind beggars. Harpies tend to work as regional reps for large companies. Typing speed 60 wpm.

Headhunter This powerful race of tribal warriors hunt alone and preserve the shrunken heads of their prey, which they display on hangers in the back of their cars when driving on motorways. Their magical abilities create an inexplicable desire in their victims to be head-hunted and a jealousy when others are hunted. In hand-to-hand combat it is impossible to defeat a headhunter.

High elf Term used to describe an elf that has risen to a senior management position. Not to be confused with an elf swinging desperately from a hot lightbulb as a set of ladders clatters to the floor below.

An Office Bestiary

Hobgoblin A smaller and slightly more pleasant sub-species of goblin (see *Goblin*). Their xenophobia is limited to off-colour jokes rather than outright prejudice.

Hydra The fangs of this many-headed serpent deliver a fatal poison. Theoretically an excellent multi-tasker, the hydra can be frozen by indecision when its heads fail to agree. Cutting off one head causes two more to grow in its place. Hat-wearing speed 12 hpm.

Imp Member of a mischievous race similar to goblins. Imps are pranksters with tendencies to befuddle but lack the social awareness to realize when a joke has gone too far. Typical imp pranks are whoopee cushions on chairs, hand buzzers, identity fraud and leaving loaf-sized poos in desk drawers. Imps shrug off disciplinary meetings and court orders with good humour. Typing speed 52 wpm.

Invisible workers A highly skilled race of unseen clerks who arrive at work half an hour before they have to and communicate only through a series of hygiene messages which they print in large letters and leave in kitchen areas. Invisible workers are thought to exist on a healthy diet of office muesli which to the untrained eye is seen to 'eat itself'. Despite having no visual form, invisible workers can be seen on dress-down Fridays, when they don their native attire of a suit and trilby, bandages and some shades.

Kobold Child-sized creature fluent in many languages, suited to catering or construction work. Kobolds possess the ability to burst into flames, although this is rarely highlighted as a key skill on their CVs.

Kraken Many-tentacled sea monster larger than a cross-Channel ferry. This pious titan is held back only by its many allergies, which include feathers, nuts and sometimes even sea. This inevitably costs companies dearly in bespoke catering. Sailor-picking speed 3 spm.

Lamb Commonly referred to in the singular as a lamby-wamby, lambs are the young of sheep (*Ovis aries*). These fluffy ruminants are herbivorous. Innocent and guileless, lambs are above suspicion in sexual-harassment tribunals.

Leprechaun A cheerful male fairy thought to hail from the Emerald Isle. Leprechauns wear huge buckled hats under which is another smaller leprechaun. Legend tells that anyone removing the second leprechaun's hat will be granted one wish – provided the wish is for a small hat. Always the first race to suggest a pub lunch on Fridays.

Leviathan Gargantuan sea serpent as old as the dawn of time, not to be confused with the Kraken (see *Kraken*). This beast of the deep is able to sink a sloop with a single swipe, which makes it a formidable squash opponent. Sailor-eating speed 7 spm.

An Office Bestiary

Lizardman   Snappy half-reptile half-human creature, highly proficient with arrows and bows. Poor thermoregulation makes this cold-blooded killer ill-suited to open-plan workspaces where office temperatures are set to suit the majority.

Magic vole   Powerful small rodent covered in soft fur. Highly skilled in arithmetic and the dark magical arts. A terrible foe. Typing speed 297 wpm.

Magical chimp   Benign monkeys wearing stripy trousers, braces and bowler hats, magical chimps have methodical minds, making them excellent at filing and cataloguing tasks. Their pleasingly gurning faces and mental acuity make them natural first-aiders. Bananas per minute: 1.

Merman   Member of an underwater race living in a traditional feudal structure with a king, knights, squires and commoners. Mermen breathe through gills and, although highly creative, are terrible procrastinators. Suited to careers in advertising.

Minertaur   Boasting the body of a black and white cow and the head of a miner, this mild-mannered beast bears many similarities to the better-known Minotaur. A fun version of the Greek classic. Cud per minute: 19.

Minotaur   Aggressive beast with the body of a man and the head of a bull. Originally the offspring of a badly thought-out holiday romance, minotaurs prefer to be held captive in labyrinths.

Nak Long-haired, tie-wearing bovine species distinguished from its cousin the yak only by its favouring of the Windsor knot. Naks are dolefully compliant and are best used to look after stands at industry fairs. Stand-minding speed 1 pm.

Needy dancer A humanoid whose gyratory confidence surges with the close proximity of another. Rhythm and soul dependant, easily devastated by office moves. See also *Private dancer*.

Ogre Humanoid giant, ugly in appearance and insatiable in appetite; most offices have at least one ogre on the payroll. Ogres can be easily identified by their large bellies, idleness and unwillingness to drink anything except diet cola. Bone-crushing speed 17 bpm.

Orc Member of a war-like race of disfigured humanoid creatures. The cruel, aggressive nature of orcs makes them formidable foes. When trapped in menial roles, orcs have a predisposition to waste company time playing office games such as carpet Frisbee, swivel-chair racing and computer-monitor Jenga.

PA Personal assistants (PAs) organize diaries, perform mail-merges, type letters and documents and field telephone calls for management-level workers and above. Despite the low-skill nature of their work, their close association with the higher workings of the office endows this race with the false conviction that they are integral to the company's success (see also Harpy). 'I-do-all-the-work-around-here' speed 60 wpm.

Parrot   Found mostly in tropical regions, this bird of the order *Psittaciformes* excels at any task that involves repetition. This makes it an excellent event planner. Pieces per minute: 8.

Pegasus   A winged steed, offspring of Poseidon (god of ocean and steeds) and the gorgon Medusa (First Ocean and Steed Lady). Pegasus sprang from the blood of Medusa when her head was cast into the Aegean Sea. Note: casting a Pegasus head into the Aegean Sea generates little more than a frenzy of gulls.

Phoenix   Firebird that makes its nest on a bed of spices, combusts and is reborn from the ashes. Low-level theft is rife in departments staffed with phoenixes. Dextrous with their wings, phoenixes are best suited to manual labour. They are easily manipulated by the promise of staff dos. Rowdy.

Photocopier   Photocopiers are best suited to administration tasks such as copying documents. Although lacking in mobility, their tough exteriors make them hardy foes. The Achilles heel of any photocopier is a weakness for jamming with paper and spilling toner.

Pirate monkey   Maritime thieves (see *Thief*), pirate monkeys are magical chimps (see *Magical chimp*) turned to crime on the high seas. Their strict dress code means that only a monkey with a minimum of one wooden appendage receives the title of pirate monkey. Social drinkers.

Pixie   This race of knee-high creatures exudes magic in the form of a dust. Pixies are renowned for leading people astray, most frequently encouraging colleagues to steal office supplies and drink more than one pint at lunchtime. Typing speed 49 wpm.

Private dancer   Dancer for money. Does what you want it to do.

Ranger   Forest- and countryside-based human who lives outside cities learning the lie of the land. Its foraging skills, along with its excellent memory, make it a formidable office 'runner' who tends never to progress past this entry-level role. Typing speed 51 wpm.

Receptionist   Guardian and greeter at the entrance gates of corporate rule. This stoic foe is practically impossible to pass using brute force but is easily paci-fied with banal small-talk. The attractiveness of a receptionist is directly proportional to her seething inner rage. Typing speed 8 wpm.

Sand fairy   Beach-dwelling earth spirits, these winged creatures have mercurial tempers and are often the butt of halfling jokes (see *Halfling*). Sand fairies can be brought back from the dead if all the children believe in them and clap their hands. Sand fairies can be sent back to the dead if they are trodden on, beheaded or poisoned.

Sea dwarf A sea-faring strain of dwarf (see *Dwarf*).

Sea gnome A gnome (see *Gnome*) on a 'sea sabbatical' organized as part of an exchange programme. For every gnome at sea, there is a bass flapping about violently on a patio.

Sea trog This brine-loving humanoid is recognized by its seaweed hair and distinctive cry of 'Bawooo-yarrr' echoing across the ocean's pitching waves. A sea trog likes to feel the spray of saltwater on its face, the roll of the sea under its feet and the comfort of a good woman in its 90 cm lobster claws. Typing speed 92 wpm.

Shapeshifter A dread creature able to take the form of any other thing. Shapeshifters use their unnatural skill to personal ends. History tells of a shapeshifter taking the form of a corpse in order to pull a convincing sickie. Their adaptability makes them first-choice candidates for implementing change in a department. Typing speed 102 wpm.

Skeletons Skeletons are the still-living bone structures of the dead. The sight of a Skeleton will quickly raise the jealous fury of a dieting ogre (see *Ogre*).

Sphinx A colossal lion with a human head. Sphinxes

display a talent for puzzles such as riddles, sudoku, word wheels and jigsaws. Excellent lateral thinkers, sphinxes are best suited to strategic roles. The word 'sphincter' derives from the same root. Riddling speed 8 rpm.

Sprite An elemental magic creature, similar in form to a pixie (see *Pixie*). Sprites may be captured using a trap made from a blackthorn branch (*Prunus spinosa*). Once ensnared, sprites can make reasonable data-entry clerks or payroll executives. Typing speed 31 wpm.

Squirrel See *Thief*.

Stork This long-beaked, long-legged wading bird belongs to the family *Ciconiidae* and feasts on insects, fish and frogs. Tradition has it that human babies are delivered by storks. Despite this recommend-ation, storks are untrustworthy in the field of postal logistics.

Tea lady Member of a race of humanoid creatures in peril of extinction. Folklore tells of a woman-like being that would magically deliver tea and snack foods to starving workers. There is a direct parallel between the legend of the tea lady and the miracle of Christ feeding the multitude at Bethsaida, causing many to believe that both events stem from the same long-forgotten source.

Thief Thieves are bastards.

An Office Bestiary

Treefolk Improbable tree-being capable of walking and talking, although it accomplishes both at ponderously slow speeds. Fiercely dull as a co-worker. Typing speed 14 wph.

Troll Divided into two species, cave dwellers and bridge dwellers, trolls are best suited to technical IT work such as server maintenance where the dark, cold environment is an ideal habitat. Trolls can be identified by their being the only species to wear their mobile phones in leather holders either on the exterior of their belts or, in extreme cases, on their wrists.

Unicorn Much like a horse, with a single horn mounted on its brow and cloven hooves. The last official sighting of this elusive creature was in Kidderminster in 1987, until it was confirmed that it was not a unicorn but a horse wearing a Cornetto. Typing speed 67 wpm.

Warg A large bear-like wolf (see *Wolf*), fierce in nature and dangerous in numbers. As a result, wargs focus on increasing their numbers at every available opportunity.

Will-o'-the-wisp Passive-aggressive ghostly fire, frequently sighted in bogs, marshes and call centres. A common trait of the will-o'-the-wisp is never to delete an email, in case it may need it to defend itself against any accusations. Typing speed 14 wpm.

Witch This race of magical hags (see *Hag*) divides

into a variety of sub-species according to the foodstuff through which they choose to perform their necromancy. The most commonly encountered witch is the Gingerbread Witch. Other witches from around the globe include the Tapas Witch, the Mezze Witch and the Wicked Witch of the Sushi. Typing speed 104 wpm.

Wizard   Throwbacks to the lad-mag culture of 1990s Britain, wizards are men endowed with magical powers who work well in all-male environments where excessive drinking and soft-core pornography are acceptable topics of conversation.

Wolf   Outspoken Gladiator (Michael Van Wijk) whose irreverent vulpine schtick cemented him a lasting role in the popular television series – unlike Diesel, Hawk, Panther, Rhino, Rio, Shadow, Trojan and the Ace.

Wraith   Faceless apparition shrouded in dark robes embodying the spirit of vengeance and death.